Chand of India

Chand of India

by IRENE MASON HARPER

Illustrated by

JEANYEE WONG

Friendship Press   New York

LIBRARY OF CONGRESS CATALOG CARD NUMBER: 54-6952

Contents

THE CHARACTERS IN THE STORY

CHAND—eleven, son of a village schoolteacher.

TARA—nine, his sister.

SRI SHERA SINGH—father of Chand and Tara. Christian teacher of the primary school in the village of Jalalabad. Usually called Master Shera or Master-ji.

KAMINI—mother of Chand and Tara. Often called Ustani-ji, which means teacher.

FRIENDS OF CHAND—Indar, Ram, Yusuf, Prem, Moti, Vijai.

FRIENDS OF TARA—Shanti, Rani, Ruth, Shirin.

ANIMALS—Nuri, the goat. Sundri, the cow-buffalo. Lali, the hen. Bambi, the baby deer.

THE REVEREND GULAM MASIH—touring pastor of the Christian congregations. Called Padre Sahib.

ROSHAN—audio-visual worker.

MR. DONNER—an American technical adviser under the Point Four Program.

MRS. DONNER—his wife.

MIKE—their son.

MR. AND MRS. GREEN—missionaries working at the Central School.

1:   The Big Day

TAN! TAN! TAN! TAN!

Chand liked to sound out the call to school. It was his regular duty, for he was the teacher's son and lived in the schoolhouse. He did not use a silly little tinkling bell like those they had in some schools. The "tan-tan" of this iron bar could be heard all over the village.

It was a heavy piece of rail that he had found one day last spring, lying in the ditch by the railroad. He had gone fishing near the railroad that wound through the scattered villages of the Punjab plain and had discovered it half buried in the earth. Some repairmen who were working on the track had said it would be all right for him to take it home. They were surprised that a boy of his age could lift it.

1

It had been a heavy load to carry, but Chand did not mind. He planned to tie a piece of wire on it and hang it on the tree in the schoolyard.

"No one else will even be able to lift it," he thought. "If any other fellow tries, he'll just crumble into pieces."

Chand was the strongest boy in the school, and he was proud of it. He could do things no one else could do. And the other boys usually recognized his right to the most important jobs.

TAN! TAN!

Chand was striking now with all his might. A few children were coming slowly from their homes. This was only the first call to school.

"Hurry up, Yusuf, and get the floor clean!" Chand shouted at the boy who was on sweeping duty.

"Don't be so bossy! I'll do the sweeping when I'm good and ready and not before. Anyway, you're calling us too early. People haven't finished eating breakfast yet."

"What's the matter with you?" Chand asked laughingly. "Have you forgotten that today is the tournament? The whole school has to get organized and ready to march off to the meet by nine o'clock. The trip to Rampur will make a long walk for the little ones."

"All right, Mr. President," jeered Yusuf. "Who made you the headman, anyway? I suppose you think you'll win all the contests. Then you'll be boss of the village, and there'll be no living with you."

Chand felt angry at these words. He clenched his fists but managed to be quiet. The tournament was more important than a quarrel. It was true that he expected to win at least one or two of the contests. He had been practicing for weeks, and last night he could hardly sleep for excitement. He thought that his *kubuddi* team was better trained than any of the other primary school teams in the district, and he had learned a new hold, in the wrestling game called *kushti,* that he was sure no one could break.

"It isn't just that I want the prizes for myself," he had assured his father the night before. "It is my duty to win for the sake of our school."

"I am sure you will," Master Shera had said. "But winning contests of strength is not the most important thing in the world, my son."

Chand had not understood what his father meant. All

he could think of was winning honors for himself and for Jalalabad.

The whole village of Jalalabad was proud of its primary school. Although there were only forty Christian families among the one hundred fifty that made up the village, it was they who had started the school. Long ago, when they had first formed themselves into a church, they began to plan for a school so that their children might learn to read the Bible. In those early days they had built for the teacher a mud hut that was better than any of their own. The teacher was Chand's father, Sher Singh, who was usually called Master Shera, and the first school was held on the bare ground under the big tree.

That was before Chand and his sister Tara were born. They could remember, though, the building of the new school. There had been great excitement when the church people brought the loads of red bricks purchased with the savings of years and worked together to build the two large rooms for the school on the end of the teacher's house.

Chand was six then, old enough to carry a small load of bricks in a basket on his head. Both he and Tara, who was then nearly four, worked in the pit where the brown earth was mixed with water for the plaster the bricklayers needed. They and the other children paddled it smooth and soft with their bare feet. It was fun!

Since that time Chand had often heard his father tell how the neighbors had taken great interest in the school and had helped by giving bricks and wood and even money. In religion the neighbors were Hindus and Sikhs who had not expected to have their children go to the Christian school. But they had liked Master Shera and so had sent their children to his school. Nowadays he often thanked God in family prayers for their friendliness and asked for wisdom to help them.

In the schoolroom Yusuf was still busy with his broom. Two girls came rushing in, throwing off their headscarves as they ran.

"Make more quickness!" they shouted to Yusuf. "How can we dust when you haven't cleaned the floor?"

Yusuf finished brushing up, and Moti, another boy on the cleaning committee, began to sprinkle the hard dirt floor with water. When the dust had settled, the girls wiped all the charts and pictures that hung on the walls, cleaned the teacher's desk, and made the bookshelves tidy.

Now that the work of cleaning was well started and the younger children had begun to gather, Chand was free for a few minutes before school prayers began. He hurried away to the yard of his friend Indar's house. There the boys had made a wrestling pit and filled it with the sand that was so plentiful around Jalalabad. Although Indar himself was a good wrestler, it was seldom that he could throw his friend.

Today Indar was waiting for Chand. The boys tossed off their shirts and tucked up their shorts. Indar threw down his turban. The long braid of his black hair was wound in a topknot on his head and pinned with a wooden comb, to show that he followed the Sikh religion. Chand's black hair bristled short and rough all over his head.

The boys faced each other, well apart, heads back, chests high, brown shoulders glistening in the hot sunshine. They bent their bodies forward from the hips. They looked like two fighting cocks.

They slapped their knees. Chand shot out his left hand to grab Indar's shoulder. But Indar dodged the thrust. They drew apart, watchful and wary. Arms swung out, blows were parried. The two wrestlers were well matched.

Indar's legs were long and thin, and he was wiry and quick. He kept his legs out of reach of Chand's hands. Chand was heavier, with bigger muscular legs and arms and a shorter reach. If he once brought a knee within Indar's grasp, he would be tossed to the ground. His best strategy was to grapple and pin Indar's arms to his sides, at the same time holding his friend's neck in the crook of his elbow. Again and again he tried the trick and failed. Suddenly he grabbed Indar. Then one of Indar's arms wiggled out, caught Chand just behind the knee, and down they both went. In falling, Chand gripped Indar's chest and turned him so that when they hit, they were side by side, and neither had won.

There was not time to fight it out. Chand's father, whom everyone called Master-ji, was now clanging the last call to school. TAN! TAN!

Chand pulled on his clean white shirt over his sweaty body as he ran. He would soon dry off in the sun. Indar, following him, thought how lucky they were that they did not have to tuck their shirts into their pants and wear belts like the American boys they sometimes saw in the movies. They had to do it, too, of course, when they wore their scout uniforms, though most of the time their shirts hung outside, wide and smooth and cool. But Indar wished he did not have to pause to wind on his turban, as Sikh boys must do.

When the boys rushed through the gate, First Class had already begun to march, singing, from the schoolyard into the neat schoolroom. Indar and Chand fell in at the end of the Fifth, which was their class and the top of the village school. After they finished Fifth Class, some of Chand's friends would go away for middle and high school. Yusuf expected to attend the Central School, where he would study for five more years, and perhaps go on to college or normal school. Chand was not so sure he wanted to go to the Central School. Of course, he knew that his father rather expected him to grow up to be a teacher and that his mother would like him to become a minister of the church. But he felt tired of school. When a fellow is almost twelve years old and a champion runner and wrestler, besides being captain of both soccer and *kubuddi* teams, he naturally has ideas other than becoming a teacher.

Prayers were rather short that morning. After the

Scripture was read and a second grader prayed, Chand's friend Prem led the national salute. While they were singing the national anthem, *"Jana, Gana, Mana,"* Chand thought, as he often did, about all the wonderful parts of India mentioned in the song. He looked at the map of India hanging on the wall in front of them.

"Assam—Punjab—Madras—Bengal—the high Himalayas—the Jumna—the Ganges—the waves of the ocean," the children sang, naming some of the great provinces, mountains, and rivers of their country. "All, all sing victory, victory to thee."

"The sights I could see if I could travel," dreamed Chand. "Delhi would be the most interesting place because that is the capital of our great new republic. I wish—"

Suddenly he realized that Master-ji was talking to the school, asking them to remember to obey the rules at the tournament.

"Perhaps some of the teams may cheat or get angry. But we who belong to a Christian school must throw our influence on the side of fair play."

A little time was spent reviewing the plans that had already been made for the day. Every pupil chose a buddy so that they could keep close together and look after each other. On the paths through the fields, they could race each other if they wanted to, but they must be careful not to trample the newly planted alfalfa nor break off the cotton blossoms. When they came to the highroad, they must watch for motor cars. "Keep to the left" was the rule. At the railway crossing, they must "stop, look, and listen." These and other rules had been learned by the whole school the day before.

At last they were off, each one carrying a little lunch tied up in a piece of cloth. How lovely the fields looked in the bright sunshine! Some were green with new shoots of grass or corn. Some were brown, ready for the sowing of wheat seed. Some were bright with yellow and white flowers on the cotton bushes. Some had tall sugar cane, almost ready to harvest.

Chand and his friends kept together. Indar was his buddy. Ram, the Hindu merchant's son, had chosen Prem, the Christian. Yusuf, the son of one of the elders of the church, looked after Moti, the youngest of the group.

"There will be a good harvest," Ram said to Indar. "My father is going to sow C_591 and C_518 in the fields where he had cotton last year. This is the best wheat seed for our soil, Master-ji says."

Chand knew that his father had advised and helped the village farmers to get the new kinds of wheat seed and cotton seed. There would be a good yield from the fields of the big landowners. Perhaps this year all the families of the church would have enough food to last till the next harvest. Most of them knew what it was like to be very hungry when the harvest was not good.

Tara and her best friend Shanti raced most of the way,

so they reached the highway before the boys. They waited for the Safety Committee. The paved road stretched far in the distance, like a ribbon of silver gray, smooth and straight and level, bordered with spreading trees. As far as the girls could see, there was no curve nor turn in the road and not even a tiny hill.

"Where does the road go?" wondered Tara. She had never traveled farther than the next town, eight miles away. She wished she could get on one of the big crowded buses that passed them, their horns shrieking.

"I wish we could go to Amritsar," she said to Shanti, "and across the border into Pakistan. That would be an adventure."

"My mother says," replied Shanti, "that she used to go often to Lahore—before our country was divided into Pakistan and India, of course. It cost only twelve annas

to go to Lahore. My grandfather still lives in Pakistan, but we have not seen him for six years."

"It is only fifty miles away," sighed Tara, "but now it is a foreign country."

The children had to walk only a quarter of a mile on the left side of the road, but in that distance, many vehicles passed them. Private cars whizzed by. Several ox carts loaded with long stalks of sugar cane creaked slowly along. Two army trucks, a man on a bicycle, three motorcycles, and a man on a camel passed the procession of schoolchildren.

Now they could see the little village of Rampur just across the highroad. The Safety Committee took charge of the crossing. All the children were silent and orderly as they marched through the narrow lanes, guided by bright colored pennants all the way to the playground.

The youngest pupils had never been to a district primary schools tournament before, and they were quite astonished at the decorations the village had put up in their honor.

On the other side of the village, a big gate of bamboo poles had been set up, decorated with branches of green leaves and many flowers. At the top of the gate was a huge red banner which read WELCOME. Ram and Chand, who knew some English, explained its meaning to the little ones. Just inside the gate was the most beautiful sight of all. A tall pole, striped with green and white and saffron, rose from a platform strewn with flower petals. High in the air was flying the largest national flag the children had ever seen.

Chand was thrilled, as he always was, at the sight of the deep green, shining white, and bright saffron colors of the flag and its Wheel of Peace and Progress. He thought of a picture he had seen of the Prime Minister, Pandit Jawaharlal Nehru, standing in front of the great Council Chamber in Delhi, with the flag flying above. Then he remembered his longing to see famous places.

"If only I could some day see the capital of my great country," he sighed.

2:   The Champion

A thousand boys and girls from fifteen village schools
sat down on three sides of the big grassy oblong where
the games and races were to be held. Those who wore
shoes took them off, but most were barefoot. They all
knew how to sit properly cross-legged, spreading their
knees and folding their feet and ankles neatly under their
thighs, so as to take up the least possible space. That was
the way they sat in school, on mats spread on the floor,
since few village schools have desks.

Master-ji was talking with some of the other teachers.
Some of them were marking out the ground for the races,
for *kubuddi,* and tug of war. The list of events was all
ready, and two of the masters were chosen to be referees.
The girls were to have a tug of war, jump rope, a three-

13

legged race, and a relay race. The boys' contests would
be a fifty-yard dash, standing broad jump, wrestling,
soccer, and *kubuddi*.

Tara and her team were in the very first event, a relay
race. They nearly lost it because Shirin had forgotten to
tie her scarf securely around her waist. It came loose and
tripped her up. But she recovered quickly, and with an
extra burst of speed made up the loss. All the boys as well
as the girls of the Jalalabad School were on their feet
shouting when Tara came in three seconds ahead of the
leader of the opposing team.

"Tara *kee Jai!* Victory to Tara!" yelled her friends.
After that, Tara's team had to run against the winners
of three other teams. They lost the very last race. Tara
led the cheering for the winning leader, "Maya *kee Jai!*"

Except for the wrestling, everyone thought that *kubuddi*

was the most exciting event. There were seven boys on each team, and they took their places on the field, on opposite sides of a white line. The referees set fifteen minutes as the time for the halves and decided which team would make the first play. Then the captain of that team chose the boy to start. The game was for each team in turn to send a player into the "home" of the other for the length of one breath, during which time he tried to keep from being caught by his opponents. In order to prove that he was not taking a breath, he had to keep saying over and over, "*Kubuddi, kubuddi,*" as fast as he could.

Chand sent out Yusuf. Taking deep breaths with chest up and head back, Yusuf ran in long leaps toward the opposite team, who were watchfully waiting. As he crossed the white line, he began to say softly and swiftly, "*Kubdee, kubdee, kubdee.*" Without pausing or taking a breath, he danced in and out, challenging different ones to tag him. Several tried to catch him, but Yusuf wiggled out of their grasp and rushed back to the line before his "breath sat down." That scored one point for Chand's team. A boy from the other side ran over to Chand's side and hopped around. He was grabbed on his way back but managed to throw his head across the line before his breath gave out. One point for his team!

Another of the Jalalabad boys went over and boldly challenged the enemy. But he was caught and thrown. When he stopped saying, *"Kubuddi"* he was "dead," and the other side scored. Two to one against Chand's team.

Now Indar went over, and he played a cautious game. He only teased the team he was challenging and ran back before he needed to. Thus the others thought he was one of the short-breath players. But Indar was saving his good chest capacity, and in the end, with the help of his strong arms and swift legs, he wiggled out of every tackle and won many points for his team. The final score stood nineteen to twelve in favor of Chand's team.

They had to play four other winning teams, and they managed to win each time. Chand and his team were very happy. They would carry home the cup and keep it for a whole year, for the honor of Jalalabad School.

Hour after hour, the games and races went on. At noon recess, the boys and girls ate the lunches they had brought. Some of them had thin bread cakes spread with good boiled butter called *ghi,* bowls of vegetable curry, and sweet pudding. Many had bread cakes with a little mustard oil and a lump of brown sugar, but some had only a couple of dry bread cakes. After lunch, the players took a long rest, lying stretched out flat on the ground. Chand took a nap, for he wanted to be strong for the wrestling, which would be the last contest.

The others wandered about the village to see the sights. Some gathered in a narrow lane to watch the blacksmith at work. His forge was out of doors in front of his shop. It was a round hole in the ground with sides built up of hard clay. The fire of charcoal, so hot that the children could not bear to come very near it, was kept glowing by the smith's small daughter pumping a big bellows. The smith was a great, strong man, with muscles bulging in his brown arms. He lifted a small piece of iron and laid it on the fire. As it began to soften in the heat, he lifted it to the forge with his tongs. Down came his huge hammer. Sparks flew, and the children jumped back. They watched fascinated, as an almost round, flat ring began to take shape.

"It looks like a horseshoe," said Moti.

"I know," explained Tara. "It is a shoe for an ox. The oxen that drag the heavy cartloads of sugar cane and cotton to the market have to wear iron shoes on their hoofs because the new paved roads are so hard."

Hanging in the dark shop were many useful things that the blacksmith had made. There were iron fire tongs of many different sizes and trowels for digging in the gardens. There were plowshares and strong hoes for the farmers.

For the kitchens there was a good supply of *tawas,* the thin, curved iron plates on which bread is baked.

"What a useful person the blacksmith is!" remarked Master Shera, who had come up just then to see that the younger children did not stray too far. "No village could get along without him."

Another workshop full of interest to the Jalalabad youngsters was the potter's. This was a large open space in front of a low mud hut. The potter needed plenty of room to spread out the newly finished clay pots and bowls in the sun. The kiln, or oven, in which he would bake them, took up a large space in the corner of the courtyard. The Fourth Class pupils were especially interested in the oven because they were planning to build a small one in their own schoolyard so that they could bake the tiny lamps they were making for Diwali. If they were nicely molded and baked perfectly, they would last for Christmas, too.

The potter had made a number of beautiful large water pots with small mouths.

"It must be very difficult to make them so perfectly round and shape the lovely, graceful neck," thought Shirin, who liked clay modeling best of all the crafts they learned in school.

The potter's wheel was a huge, round stone set over a shallow pit in the ground. The potter, sitting with his feet in the pit, spun the wheel rapidly while his skillful fingers shaped the smooth, whirling clay. The children watched

him take up balls of well kneaded clay and rapidly shape them into plates and small bowls.

"There is to be a grand wedding," explained the potter's wife. "The headman's daughter is to be married, and these dishes are to be used for the feast."

Everyone knows that hundreds of dishes are needed for a Hindu feast because the plates and bowls in which food is served to guests are always smashed and thrown away afterwards.

Many children lingered under the banyan tree. This spreading umbrella of thick leaves made a wonderful temple of shade in the very center of the village. The children ran in and out of the aisles formed by the twisted roots that sprang from the enormous low branches and reached down to the ground. Many of the village people thought that this strange and lovely tree was sacred. They worshiped it and prayed to it to save them from smallpox and other evils or to bring them good luck.

"Come, girls and boys," called Master Shera at last. "It is time to go back to the playground. Suppose you sing a song, to keep us all together. Shanti and Tara, you know the Punjabi song about the singing trees."

Shanti and Tara and a few others sang a couplet, then led the rest in repeating it.

The pipal sings; the banyan sings;
And the green mulberry, too.

Stop, traveler, and listen.
Your soul will be set right.

"I know two other couplets about the banyan," said Prem to Master-ji as they walked along. "Do you like these?"

Under the banyan tree,
I happened to see Almighty God.

The banyan knows the secrets,
No good telling lies in its presence.

"Good," said Master-ji, "let's paint those on the schoolroom wall, along with a picture of a spreading banyan tree."

After the noon rest, all the girls' schools competed in the tug of war. In the finals, just as Tara felt the tug moving in her direction, she saw a little girl onlooker come close and thrust her foot slyly in to brace her friend's foot, and suddenly the line of struggling girls pulled strongly the other way. The whistle blew, for the referee had seen the trick. Tara and her team were so angry that they easily won in the next try. This gave them the championship.

Chand's team was beaten early in the soccer matches, but they felt all right about it because Indar had made second in the fifty-yard dash, and they were sure Chand would win first place in wrestling. Chand knew that this would be his real test.

Excitement was high, for this contest always called out the biggest and strongest boys in the primary classes. Chand took on all comers. With his new, quick twist of the shoulders which brought a knee within his reach, he threw the champions of three big schools very quickly. The fellow he dreaded most was disqualified for twisting the wrist of his opponent.

The last match was desperate. Back and forth the wrestlers struggled, breathing hard and almost exhausted in the heat of the afternoon sun. Chand kept his temper when his opponent broke the rules by trying to trip him up. The referee had not seen, but it made Chand more wary. Suddenly he seized the boy's chest and arms with an extra powerful grip, pulled up a knee—and—flat they both were on the ground, with Chand on top. Pandemonium broke loose. Every last spectator was yelling, "Chand, Chand, Chand, *kee Jai!*"

The masters had a hard time getting the children quieted down for the prize-giving. Every school got some award. But little Jalalabad School won a small silver plaque for entering the largest number of contests. A silver cup for the tug-of-war championship was carried home by the girls to be kept till the next tournament. A similar cup was carried off by the boys for *kubuddi*. Chand won the award for being the best captain—his prize, a Bharat Scout manual. Indar received one rupee as second prize in running, and Chand's prize for first place in wrestling was two rupees. The tournament ended in good spirits. Even those who had lost began to plan how they would win next year. Tara and Shirin and Shanti resolved to practice running every day.

Master-ji had some trouble keeping the excited children in order on the long walk home. When they came near the village, they broke ranks and swarmed around Chand. They lifted him to the shoulders of Indar and Prem. Little Moti held his feet, and Yusuf led the procession shouting and waving as they entered the school compound. Tara ran into her mother's arms.

"Chand won everything!" she murmured proudly and happily.

That evening both Tara and Chand were too excited

to sleep. They talked about what Chand would do with the two rupees he had won.

"I shall keep it to go traveling," Chand decided.

"Take me, too," begged Tara. "I do so want to go to Amritsar and see the Golden Temple."

"Amritsar nothing!" retorted Chand scornfully. "I mean to go to Delhi."

Tara went into the schoolroom to get the new copy of "The Treasure Chest," which had just come that day. There was a good story about Delhi, with pictures. She read to Chand until Mother called for them to go to sleep.

"Do you know what, sister?" Chand's voice was drowsy. "I intend to be a great wrestler when I grow up. I'll go to Delhi. Then I'll win a place on the Olympic Team. Wah, wah! I shall travel all over the world and win first place for India. I might even go to America."

But as he dropped off to sleep, Chand wondered what his father had meant when he said that winning championships was not the most important thing in the world.

3:   Chand's Disappointment

A hard week was ahead of Chand. The Fifth Class tests were coming, and these were important to him.

On Saturday he hoped to be initiated into the patrol of the Bharat Scouts. He was now almost twelve and had been a Wolf Cub for years. He had already passed the Tenderfoot test, but his father, who had organized the village patrol and was the scoutmaster, would not allow him to join until he could show a better record in his schoolwork. Winning championships in wrestling and being captain of the team was not getting him anywhere with Master-ji. So this was the week for Chand to work hard on arithmetic and Hindi in all his spare time.

It was just his luck that a big holiday was coming that week, Chand thought. Everyone was getting ready for

Diwali, the Feast of Lights. There would be a program at the school and lots of fun in the village. He expected that Ram would be chosen program leader instead of himself, while Tara and the girls would do most of the decorating.

Chand hated to be left out of the fun. Diwali is a Hindu festival that comes in the autumn and heralds many months of bright sunshine. The Christian school joined in the Hindu celebration to show their good will, just as the Hindu children took part in the celebration of Christmas.

The younger children were dabbling in wet clay, making little lamps called *diwas*. The older classes had built a small oven just like the one the potter used to bake his bowls. When they had finished baking the little clay saucers, they would fill them with oil and put in a little wick made from a string or piece of cloth, and light them on Diwali. Master Shera was painting a new border on the whitewashed walls above the blackboards. He painted a long row of little lamps, and they made a pretty design.

In Bible lesson, the children learned about the ancient lamps of Palestine and compared their shape with the *diwas*. The story was about the ten foolish bridesmaids who forgot the oil for their lamps. Fourth Class made a play out of it.

On Diwali, which came on Tuesday, Tara and her friends put on their prettiest clothes—ruffled pantalets and long flowered *kurtas*. There was a short program in school, with songs, essays, poems, and the Fourth Class play. Ram was the leader, just as Chand had thought.

First Class sang "Shine, Shine Like Stars," while they held up big stars cut from white paper. One of the stars even had a silver border made of bits of candy wrappings.

After the program, the big boys filled the clay saucers with oil, laid in the wicks, and placed the tiny lamps along the edges of the flat roof of the schoolhouse, all ready for the evening. The rest of the morning they spent playing games.

In the late afternoon Chand settled down to study alone in the schoolroom, while Tara and the other children wandered about the bazaar looking at the wonderful sweets and toys in the shops. There were castles and boats and chariots made of spun sugar in many lovely colors. All kinds of brightly painted toys, some of them animals, some Hindu gods and goddesses, were sold in the shops. The rich man of the village, Ram's father, gave sweets to all the children. Tara took some home to Chand, who was having a hard time keeping his mind on his lessons.

At dusk, the bigger boys climbed up on the flat roof of the schoolhouse and lighted the *diwas*. How wonderful it looked! The school and the teacher's house were outlined with dozens of tiny twinkling flames. Chand left his studies and came outside to see the sights for a little while.

All over the village the lights were lit. The house of Ram's father was decorated with hundreds of big and little candles, not only on the roofs, but outlining the arches and the doors and windows. The boys all admired the grand display, but Ram said, "Pooh! It's nothing. You ought to see my uncle's house in Delhi. On Diwali he turns on dozens of colored electric bulbs. They have electricity there, and my cousin-brothers study their lessons by electric light instead of by old smoky lanterns the way we have to."

Chand was sick of hearing Ram brag about Delhi. He was feeling rather cross this evening because he had missed most of the fun, so he said sharply, "Listen to the Lat Sahib. He is always talking about Delhi as if he owned it. I suppose you'll be going to Delhi again, so you can boast some more."

"Well, I am going, smarty," retorted Ram in an angry voice. "In January I'm going to Delhi for Republic Day. Just you try and stop me!"

"I have heard," said Prem to change the subject and keep trouble from brewing, "that when the Bhakra Dam is finished, all our villages in this area will have electricity."

"By the time we finish high school, I expect it will be the ordinary thing to use electricity for our homes and our village workshops," said Indar in a tone full of wonder.

Chand had to leave and go back to study by the light of the old lantern. "No electric light—and no Delhi for me," he thought bitterly.

The rest of that week, while Chand was studying, Tara was learning some new games. It was early November, and the weather was so cold that the children could not sit inside the schoolrooms, even with their coats on. Some of them had only thin jerseys to wear as their warm clothes. But in the sun it was always warm, so the classes were held outside, and they hardly needed coats.

The girls' games were very lively. Tara's friends were so elated over their tug-of-war victory that they would play nothing but games of strength. One of the funniest was "Take a Squash." The players sat in a line on the ground, each with her arms around the waist of the one in front and legs gripped close on either side. Two girls were Shoppers, and they came along looking carefully at the long line of Squashes bound closely together. They chose one and tried to pull her loose. Each Squash that was pulled off the string became a Shopper.

Tara's favorite game was "Old Woman." In this the girls took a head scarf—boys take a turban—and tied together the right elbow and the right knee of the one who was It. Then It had to hop around and tag someone.

Two days after Diwali, the Fifth Class tests began. The school year begins in April, and it was now half finished. For two days, Thursday and Friday, the children took written examinations in arithmetic, geography, history, hygiene, everyday science, Hindi, and Punjabi.

Chand did not worry much about geography and history. The wonders of travel and the stories of Indian heroes were easy for him to remember. The history of the long struggle for independence was exciting. He liked to learn about the new government that had its headquarters in the part of the capital called New Delhi.

Learning about his body and how to keep it strong and healthy was also interesting to an athlete. The book "Keep Healthy" told about all the common diseases—malaria, typhoid, plague, tuberculosis, and smallpox—and how to fight them. Chand was always ready for a fight. It was fun to wage war on the mosquitoes and to organize the children into an army to get vaccinated or inoculated against cholera.

But arithmetic and composition and poetry were a much harder battle for Chand. He had to fight them with pen and pencil. He was having a hard time, too, with

everyday science, which was all about how a pulley works and the food values of different vegetables and how to grow them. Chand was rather bored with science and agriculture.

To Tara, the two days of exams seemed very long. Suppose Chand failed! She knew their father would mark the papers very strictly, and if Chand did not get a passing mark in every single subject, he would not be allowed to join the scouts. On Saturday at school the results of the examinations would be announced. Each night Tara watched her father marking papers, but she did not dare to ask him anything.

When school was dismissed at noon on Saturday for the half holiday, Master-ji announced that Chand and most of his classmates had passed. His hard study had been worth while, Chand felt.

In the afternoon, Chand went proudly with his father to his first meeting of the Bharat Scouts. It was held at Ram's house, for Ram's father was the one who had asked Master Shera to organize the village patrol, and he was always ready to help.

When Chand returned home, Tara was eager to hear about the meeting. But she had not expected such exciting news as he had to tell.

"The scouts are planning a trip to Delhi to celebrate Republic Day," he told her. "That was really what Ram was bragging about on Diwali."

"A trip to Delhi!" cried Tara. "Oh, Chand, how wonderful! You have wanted so much to go. You will spend your two rupees prize on that, I suppose."

Chand's voice was sad. "Two rupees are not nearly enough. The railway fare even with concession allowed for school excursions will be seven rupees, eight annas.

"The boys will take their food for the first day, but three days in the city and a day coming back will cost at least six rupees for food, and we must have bus fares and something for lodging. We figured that each member would need eighteen rupees for the trip."

Tara's face fell.

"Oh, dear! You can never earn that much before

January. Will Father go? He can't afford it, either."

"Ram's father has offered to pay the scoutmaster's expenses. But Father says I shall have to wait till next year."

"That will never do," said Tara to herself. "There must be some way to raise the money."

"Let's see." Tara brought her slate and pencil. She was good at arithmetic. "Republic Day is on January 26. Let us count the weeks from now till then."

They got down from the wall the big calendar with Prime Minister Nehru's picture on it. They found that, counting out Christmas week, there would be nine Saturday half-holidays in which Chand could work. And perhaps in Christmas week they might get two or three days to work.

"You ought to be able to earn at least seven annas cutting grass for cattle fodder on Saturday, and I can earn four annas. I can't work as long as you because, of course, I have to help Mother, and you only have to feed Sundri and Nuri. Let's see! That makes seven and four are eleven."

Tara was busily writing on her slate and talking to herself. "Nine times eleven annas makes ninety-nine annas. Ninety-nine divided by sixteen makes six rupees and three annas." She had the answer in a second because she knew her "sixteen times" tables so well. There are sixteen annas in a rupee, so Indian children have to learn their multiplication table up to sixteen times.

"Then perhaps you can earn two rupees in Christmas

week, and if anybody gives me a rupee for Christmas, I'll give it to you. And with the two rupees you have won, that will make eleven rupees and three annas," she finished triumphantly.

"Very good!" Chand's tone was sarcastic. He was so discouraged he forgot to appreciate Tara's unselfish interest. "But where will the other seven rupees come from?"

"Not seven rupees, only six rupees and thirteen annas," insisted Tara.

She ran off then to help her mother fix the vegetable curry and bake the bread cakes for their evening meal. As she ground the yellow turmeric powder and mixed in the red peppers and the garlic, she could hear Chand muttering bitterly while he brought the piles of greens for the cow and the goat.

"Oh, yes! We're just poor people! And we will be poor until I earn a lot of money at wrestling or something. You'd better believe I'm never going to be a teacher like Father or a preacher like Padre Sahib. Teachers and preachers are always poor."

Mother was very sympathetic, but she had no suggestion to make. Already she had decided to do without the winter coat she needed, and patch her old thin one, in order to buy Chand's scout uniform and Tara's pretty blue scarf and her white slacks and *kurta* for the Bulbul Flock, which is like a Brownie group.

Suddenly Tara had what she thought was a bright idea. She took a long breath before she explained it to her mother. She knew that every month when Father got his salary from the mission, he counted out six rupees, "the Tenth Part," and put it into Mother's box marked "The Lord's Money." This was used for the church and for helping the poor and was never touched for any other purpose.

Chand came in from his chores just as Tara put her question.

"Couldn't we borrow six rupees from the tithe?" she asked in a small voice because she knew her mother would be shocked. "Chand and I could easily earn it and pay it back in February and March."

"Little daughter," said Kamini, kindly, "perhaps you don't realize that five rupees of our tithe go to the church to pay our share of our pastor's salary. Our family must set a good example in church self-support. If our little church and all the others that our Padre Sahib serves do not pay regularly, he will not get enough to eat. Then how can he travel on his bicycle and visit twenty village Christian groups every two weeks?"

"I know, I know," muttered the little girl, "but this is our own money—and—and—we need it just for a few months."

"Do you know where Father's salary comes from?" answered Kamini. "A church school in the United States gives it every month because they want to help the boys and girls of India to have an education. We like to believe when we get this money that it means they are thinking of us in a friendly way. We are thankful and pray for these generous givers. They help us to serve this village in Christian love. But we don't think we should ask them to support our church and our pastor. We are trying to do that ourselves. And our family tithe must go for that purpose."

So that was that! Tara felt that there was no hope of Chand's seeing the wonders of Delhi this year.

4:   New Adventure

It was not easy for Chand to give up the idea of the trip to Delhi. For a time all the fun of being a member of the scouts was spoiled. He lost his interest even in the things he liked to do. Father had to speak sharply to him, not only because he was neglecting his lessons but also because he often forgot to feed Nuri and Sundri.

Tara tried to help her brother all she could. If she heard Nuri bleating when she went out to look after Lali and her brood of chicks, she would run quickly to get an armful of mustard greens before her brother's neglect was noticed.

Chand took to walking off alone through the farther fields, in the early evening, mooning over his troubles. A longing to go away, to walk on and on towards the sunset, to travel somewhere, grew stronger and stronger.

"Escape! Escape!" he muttered. "If only the minstrels would come! I could slip away with them and go singing through the villages. I want to see the world—and I will—I will."

The wandering minstrels usually came at least once a year. Gaily they would stroll into the village, carrying their beautiful instruments, singing snatches of popular songs. In a minute they would be surrounded by children and by young men coming in from the work of the fields. At dusk, they would light a flare torch soaked in mustard oil and hold it aloft on a long bamboo. Through all the lanes they would march, waving the torch and calling the people to the concert. When Chand was little, his mother could not keep him in bed when the minstrels were around. He would slip away and squeeze into the crowd seated in a circle on the ground.

In the center would sit the musicians cross-legged, each with his precious *sitar* or other stringed instrument cradled carefully in his lap. The sweetest sounds came from the slender flutes, but the most stirring and exciting rhythms were beaten out on both ends of the long drum. Sometimes one of the men, pleased at hearing Chand's sweet, clear voice singing in the crowd, would let him have a try clapping the cymbals or shaking the tambourines.

Once the minstrels had taken him away with them. That had been two years ago. Chand had gone home after the concert with his father and mother. But, after they were asleep, he had slipped out to be with the minstrels and had sung with them till dawn. The men had said that a boy with such a fine voice could easily earn his living making folks happy with music. Chand was thrilled to be invited to join their troupe and went off with them. He felt very grown up, tramping from village to village and sleeping out under the stars. He learned to tune the big drum by tightening the leather thongs, and he started to learn to blow the flute. He spent a happy three days with the minstrels before his father found him and brought him home. Now his musical wandering was only a memory.

One Saturday evening Chand was dreaming about the minstrels as he lay under a mango tree and watched the stars come out and twinkle through the broad green leaves. He idly noticed a figure approaching on a bicycle along the sandy road. Suddenly he was aroused by a familiar voice.

"Chand. Wake up! How about a good singing party tonight?" Standing over him was Padre Gulam Masih, the pastor of their little church, who came every two weeks to hold services.

Singing was what Chand liked best about the pastor's visit. He jumped up quickly.

"*Namaste,* Padre Sahib," he said in greeting, putting his hands together and giving the graceful Indian bow. "I'll call the young men. I have the small drums ready."

Master Shera was happy to welcome the pastor. Kamini was just baking the bread. Tara quickly brought a clean leaf for a plate and a good portion of lentils, and two hot, fresh bread cakes were laid on it. After asking God's blessing, they all ate heartily, sitting close to the good fire.

The singers soon gathered, and the young pastor led them in singing many new and old Christian hymns, playing the two small drums, which he stood upright between his knees. Several of the new songs were practiced over and over. This one, or that one, the Padre told them, would be good to sing when folks asked about the Christian religion.

In the morning Tara and Chand made ready for the Sunday worship. They had to turn the schoolroom into a church. They hung up one of their precious Bible pictures and arranged pink and white cosmos from their school garden in a brass bowl on a small table. They put the sitting mats on the floor with special care, so that the place would be orderly for the Lord's Day.

At church Padre Gulam Masih preached on the text, "Be strong and let your heart take courage, all you who wait for the Lord!" He said the best way he could explain about how God helps us was to tell about his own experience.

"When I was quite a big boy, my father and his neighbors in our village of Pakistan learned about Jesus Christ who came to the world to bring us close to God. They heard the call of Christ and decided to be his followers. I, too, gave my heart to Jesus, and took the name of Gulam Masih, slave of Christ.

"When I finished high school in Sialkot, I felt that Christ wanted me to work among some of the poorest Christians. So, instead of going back to my own home village, I started a little school in a village near the Sutlej River, where a number of families had recently become Christian. Very soon after that, India became a republic, and the Punjab was divided into two parts. The village where I was teaching was near the border on the Pakistan side. Terrible things began to happen. All over the country, Muslims tried to drive out the Hindus and Sikhs, and across the line, in India, the Hindus and Sikhs did the same to the Muslims. People who had been neighbors began to hate one another. There was a lot of fighting and many were killed.

"The Christians in that village were terrified. They hid in their mud huts. It seemed to me that this was a time for us Christians to be bold and brave and try to stop the fighting, or at least to help our neighbors who were hurt. I talked and prayed with the new Christians, and God gave them courage. They went into the homes and bound up the wounds of Muslims, Hindus, and Sikhs. Finally we, too, were driven out and escaped across the border into India and went to a village near the mission hospital. There we were able to help the sick and wounded along the highroad that led in and out of Pakistan. I got medicines from the mission doctors, and they taught me how to help."

Chand listened eagerly to the story. He thought that the pastor must be a very brave man, although he looked small and thin. He could never be a champion in sports, of course. But still, he had acted like a champion. Chand brought his attention back to the pastor's words.

"All during this awful time, I felt so sure that God, our Father, was taking care of us. It seemed as if I heard him say to me, 'Be strong and let your heart take courage.' I decided to be one of his ministers and I went to theological seminary and learned to be a pastor. Now I am so happy because more and more people are asking about the Christian way, and are hearing the call of Jesus.

"The church in my home village back in Pakistan is growing strong, too. My father is still the leader in it. We here must pray for our Christian brethren in Pakistan and ask God to give them courage in their poverty and persecution. May God help us to bring in his kingdom in our own village and in all the world!"

Padre Sahib had to leave at noon, as he planned to visit two other villages that day. Before he left, he had a plan to talk about with Master Shera. It concerned the people working up at the headwaters of the Sutlej River, where with the help of the United States Point Four Program, the government of India is building one of the greatest dams in the world. American engineers have come to work with the Indian engineers. Thousands of workmen are digging and building at a place called Nangal.

Tara and Chand were listening eagerly because they had read in their paper "The Treasure Chest" about the Bhakra-Nangal Project.

"There are at least ten thousand people up there and only a few of them have even heard of Jesus and his Good News," explained Padre Gulam Masih enthusiastically. "Our plan is to go up there every other Sunday to preach and help in a friendly way. Next week end, Roshan, the president of the youth fellowship of our United Church, will drive to Nangal and show a moving picture of the life of Jesus.

"Here is where you can help, Master-ji," went on the pastor. "Roshan and I need a boy to help set up the machine and run errands. It is a long trip, and it won't be easy. We need a strong, brave boy"—Chand held his breath and could hardly believe his ears—"and especially one with a good, clear voice, who can sing the Christian songs to that big crowd. That is why we have chosen your son as our helper. Will you allow him to go?"

"Would you like to do this service, Chand?" asked his father.

Would he! Chand's eyes sparkled. This was the most wonderful thing that had ever happened to him. How glad he was that the minstrels had not come last night! He might have gone off with them and missed this. He could hardly wait to start.

Next Friday noon Chand was off. He had to walk two miles to the highroad, carrying a roll of two blankets on his head and a bundle of food in his hand. There Roshan and Padre Sahib were waiting in the pickup truck.

Fifty miles from home they began to see the hills. They

went bumping over rough roads and plowing through the sandy beds of two dried up rivers, until far off on the horizon appeared the dim, purple clouds that Roshan said were the foothills of the mountains. Soon the road was winding among piles of great smooth stones, the like of which Chand had never seen in his life.

They passed big factories where Indian workmen were making parts for machinery. They saw new villages built of bricks, electric powerhouses and wonderful, deep, concrete canals that would carry water to thousands of acres of barren land. Just above the town they could see a rocky gorge cut between two towering hills. Chand had looked at pictures of mountains in school, but he had never imagined he would actually see them.

"Now you can see the Sutlej River way up in that ravine between the high rocks," explained Roshan. "When the Bhakra Dam is finished, all the water of that river will be turned into the new canals."

They came to the town of Nangal, and Roshan stopped to see Mr. Donner, his American friend.

Mr. Donner was a very tall man wearing a heavy sweater and khaki pants. Chand was surprised. Somehow he had thought that Americans would be dressed in very rich clothes. He had expected to feel frightened and shy, but when Mr. Donner greeted Roshan in a friendly way and shook hands with Padre Gulam Masih, he felt different. Chand held out his hand and said, "How do you do, sir," as his father had taught him.

"Hello, what have we here?" Mr. Donner had a twinkle in his eye. "A boy who can speak English. You and Mike will be friends."

Chand tried to say that he knew only a little English, but just then a young memsahiba in a bright yellow dress rushed out of the house. Behind her came a boy about Chand's size. The lady folded her hands quite properly and said, *"Namaste"* in a merry voice and then held out her hand to each of them. Chand was careful to take her hand in both of his and bow very respectfully, as he had seen the Padre Sahib do. The two boys just stared at each other.

"Chand, this is Mike," said Mr. Donner.

"We'll not ask you into the house now," Mrs. Donner said to Roshan. "It is after five, and you must get your supper and set up your screen and machine before dark. Sri Samuel, a young Christian overseer, is going to look after you at his house. I hope you all sleep well tonight. In the morning we shall go to the Bhakra Dam, and I shall expect you all for lunch and to spend the afternoon in our home."

"Thank you very much, Mrs. Donner," said Roshan. "We shall enjoy that. Come, Chand. Padre Sahib and I must find Sri Samuel."

There was plenty to do. Sri Samuel gave them good food and told them about the little Christian group among the workers on the dam and in the factories. They were trying hard to teach others about Christ and had found some who were interested. There would probably be more than two thousand people gathered to see the movie.

The pastor and Chand were very much surprised to find a beautiful, modern high school building in Nangal. The picture was to be shown in the yard between the two wings of the school. Chand climbed up to the roof to help fix the ropes that held up the big portable screen they had brought in the pickup. There was plenty of electric power at Nangal, so there was no difficulty about connecting the microphone, and the pictures were bright and clear.

The audience, seated on the ground, were very quiet as they watched, spellbound. The whole story of the gospel was pictured upon the screen. Chand knew the story of the life of Jesus, of course, but he had never been able to picture it clearly in his mind. Here he saw it acted out before his very eyes. There was Jesus, walking with his disciples, gathering the children in his arms, healing the blind and those who had leprosy.

All the explanation and the conversation were in Punjabi and given by Roshan through the loud-speaker, so that those who watched could understand what they saw.

In the last part, when Jesus was beaten as he wore the crown of thorns, one could hear a great sigh go up from the crowd. When the disciples learned that Jesus was alive, the audience clapped with joy. Afterwards many came up to ask questions, and Padre Sahib promised to meet with them on Saturday and Sunday for further conversation.

While Roshan was carefully putting away his films and apparatus, Chand asked him, "Is this stuff very expensive? How do you have money enough to own it?"

"I do not own it. It belongs to the mission, and it is my job to run it and take care of it. It is a wonderful job. I travel all over the country and show this and other pictures to thousands of people who have never heard of Christ. Oh, yes, it is very expensive. I have to take good care of it and keep it and the motor car in order. The pickup, the picture machines, the other apparatus, and a supply of films cost many rupees. Christian young people in America raised the money and sent it to show their friendliness for our people. I wish they could be here and see what it is doing."

Chand wondered whether he would like to drive the truck and show pictures as Roshan did, but he decided that he would still prefer to travel over India as a champion in sports.

5: A New Friend

Next morning Mrs. Donner with Michael came to take them to Bhakra Dam. She was driving the Donner car, which they had brought with them from America. She said Mr. Donner had gone to work early and they would meet him up the river where he was overseeing the boring of holes in the rocks by the shore. She made Chand sit in front with Mike and herself so she could practice speaking his language. Roshan and Padre Sahib sat in back, with Sri Samuel, the Christian overseer.

Mrs. Donner was a good driver, and she kept them all interested with her lively talk. Roshan translated some for Chand's benefit. Then Mrs. Donner would listen and repeat some of the words.

"Teach me how to say 'mountain,'" she insisted.

"*Pahar, pahar, pahar,*" she said over and over again in Punjabi. "See, Mike, that's the way to learn Chand's language."

"Now, Chand, you say 'mountain' in English," and she made him repeat it until he learned it.

After a while, Mike and Chand caught on and had lots of fun shouting words at each other.

" 'Big,' " Mike would say. "*Barra,*" Chand would reply.

Then Mike would say "*barra*" and Chand would say "big."

Then they went on to say "*pani*" for "water," which Mike already knew, and "engine," which Chand knew.

They were driving on a narrow, twisting road high above the river. Every few minutes Mrs. Donner had to pull the car to the left over piles of rock to let a big, loaded truck go by. Sometimes it would seem as if their car would go over the dizzy edge.

"Now look up," said Mike, nudging Chand and pointing ahead.

Two rocky peaks loomed against the sky. Between them was a narrow gorge cut by the river. Mrs. Donner stopped the car and they got out. They tried throwing stones down to the shining ribbon of river below. Soon they saw Mr. Donner with a group of workmen at the edge of the river. He came climbing up over the rocks. His clothes were muddy and his face streaked with sweat.

"Want to know what we are doing down there?" he began. "Well, I'm going to put in a big drill that will bore 200 feet into the rock of the river bed. Then I'll get samples of all the different layers of rock and soil. When I have tested them, I'll know how strong the foundation of the dam must be. There'll be a lot of figuring to do, and believe me, we can't afford to make any mistakes. We have to be good at mathematics," he finished, winking at Mike.

When Roshan had explained it to Chand in Punjabi, Mr. Donner went on.

"Look up at those two high spurs. How would you like to be here when they tumble into the river? Well, that's what they're going to do. We're going to plant about fifty-five tons of dynamite inside those hills, just enough to move them, and in a minute or two they'll be gone! It will take a lot of paper work and planning to calculate just the right amount of dynamite to use, not too much and not too little, and to get everyone out of the way in time, so they won't get hurt. But that's not my job—that's in another department.

"The machines and instruments are being sent out from the United States for this dam," he went on. "Do you know that this is the biggest construction project now going on in the whole world?"

Chand felt a thrill of pride. Such a big undertaking for a new country!

Now they were told to look to the left and the right of the river at the base of the two hills. There they saw what seemed like two round holes. They were the outlets of tunnels that had been built through the rock. The other ends were near the river in the valley above. The plan was to make the river bed dry in the gorge before the dam was begun. The water of the river would be turned into these tunnels and come out below, emptying into canals.

Mr. Donner hopped on the running board while his wife drove them near the mouth of the right-hand tunnel. Mike suggested that they walk through the tunnel, which was half a mile long. Chand and Roshan wanted to go. But before they started, Mr. Donner told them more about the dam.

"The top of it will be almost as high as those peaks. It will fill all this space of the gorge. At the bottom it will be 500 feet thick and more than 700 feet wide, and it will slant up to the top, which will be 40 feet thick. You can see that the foundation we have to plan will have to be mighty strong to support that tremendous concrete structure. Do you know, boys, that the dam will be 680 feet high, the second highest in the world?"

"Yes," added Mike. "The Hoover Dam is the highest—over four times as high as Niagara Falls—but our dam is only a few feet lower than it is."

Mr. Donner had to leave them then. The boys walked through the tunnel and the car met them at the upper end. They saw a pretty valley spread out before them and a peaceful little village on the bank of the river.

"When the dam is built and the tunnels closed off," explained Mrs. Donner, "this whole valley will be filled with water. This village will be moved to a safe place

below the dam. The water in the reservoir will supply the water power to run the huge dynamos that will make electricity. In all, there will be about fifty powerhouses in the whole system, all run by the great Sutlej River. A hundred and fifty towns and thousands of villages will have electric lights."

Chand noticed gangs of workmen high on both slopes of the hills and asked what they were doing. Several big trucks were toiling up the rough, winding roads. Mike explained that this was the road building department. Roads had to be built to the top in order to carry up the dynamite to plant at different places in the rocks. Mrs. Donner drove near a huge bulldozer plowing through the earth and rocks and cutting a road like magic. In another place a Euclid truck was parked.

"I never saw such a big truck in my life!" gasped Roshan.

Mike and Chand were out of the car in a moment and climbing up onto the seat of the Euclid. Mike honked the horn and a tremendous sound echoed through the valley.

"Here comes my friend, Sri Narain," said Mike joyfully. "He is the head of the road building department. My father says he is one of the cleverest engineers he ever met."

Mike's friend good-naturedly explained the fine points of the Euclid and let the boys ride with him while he started the powerful Diesel engine and roared down the slope.

At last it was time to pick up Mr. Donner and drive back to the Donner home. The travelers were tired and quite ready for lunch.

There were many wonders to see in the pleasant house the Indian government had built for the Americans. There was a refrigerator, an electric stove, and a washing machine. Chand was full of wonder, but all the time he was worrying about eating with Mike's family. He thought that they would probably all sit together at a table, but he knew nothing at all about their customs and manners of eating. From the English primer he knew a few useful words like "spoon" and "fork."

"Don't worry," Roshan told him, "just watch what Mike does and try to act like him."

Fortunately, they had what Mrs. Donner called an Indian meal. It consisted of a dish of rice and peas called *kichri,* a curry made of spiced bits of meats, and the thin bread cakes called *chapatties*. Chand tried to use a fork with the rice, but Mrs. Donner told him to eat it his own way. In the end they all learned to mix the *kichri* and curry with their fingers and pick it up with a piece of bread. But only Chand and Padre Sahib and Roshan did it properly without soiling their fingers above the second joint. They had ice cream for dessert, and Chand liked it very much.

"*Bahut accha,* very good," he said, and Mike and Mrs. Donner learned to say it, too.

After lunch, at his mother's suggestion, Mike showed Chand his stamp collections. Roshan was interested, too. They looked at albums of stamps from all over the world. This was right in Chand's line. Although he had only a few stamps in his collection back home and had made his album himself from an old exercise book, he could read the names on some of Mike's stamps, and he knew a little about some of the countries they came from. Roshan explained to Mike how interested Chand was in travel, so Mike showed him some picture post cards of the big steamer on which they sailed from New York, of sights in London and Gibraltar, Malta, Port Said, Aden, Karachi, and Bombay. He got out a small globe from his school cupboard, and they traced the journey.

"Have you been to Delhi?" asked Chand.

Mike shook his head and asked Roshan to explain his answer.

"We haven't seen Delhi yet. But after Christmas we

are going to have an apartment in New Delhi and we will live there for two months. I guess that will be interesting."

Then Mike brought out a bag of coins. He had money from several different countries, but Chand was most interested in seeing those of the United States. With Roshan's help, he reckoned out the values—a dollar is nearly five rupees, a dime is nearly eight annas, a nickel is nearly four annas, an anna is worth more than a cent. Mike had questions to ask about Indian money, especially the little copper coins called pice, which are four to an anna. He could see how much harder arithmetic would be in India, where the money was in sixteens and fours instead of hundreds and tens. He asked Chand how many annas would be in fourteen rupees and the answer came instantly—224.

Mike's greatest treasures were some old silver dollars. One was marked 1879. "Before my grandfather was born," said Mike. Chand thought about a Victoria rupee that Ram, the merchant's son, had. Wouldn't it be fun to give Mike a Victoria rupee as old as his American dollar? Chand wondered if he had some treasure he could trade with Ram for the rupee. He would almost be willing to swap the penknife that Mr. Green had given him for Christmas. He was pretty sure that Ram would give up the old coin in exchange for that.

Mrs. Donner came in then and showed some pictures of their home in Michigan. One picture showed Mike standing with a fine-looking heifer.

"He got a prize for his calf at the county fair," she explained. "He took care of the calf from the time she was born."

"I named her Beauty," interrupted Mike.

"My buffalo is named Sundri, which means 'beautiful,' " said Chand.

After a while they went over to the playground near the school where a group of boys about their age were playing games. Mike did not know the games, but he and Roshan urged Chand to join in.

Soon Chand was in the midst of an exciting *kubuddi* game and, of course, his side won. Mike got quite excited when he saw that his friend was the best player there.

Roshan explained about the primary schools tournament and Chand's success in it. After that, Mike insisted on seeing a wrestling match. Chand took on the biggest boy and threw him, after quite a struggle.

"Oh, boy! Won't I tell the fellows at home about my friend the champion!" thought Mike.

Soon it was time to get ready for the moving pictures. Roshan was going to show some new ones—"Dust or Destiny," which was all about science and God; "Peace or War"; and an animated cartoon "How Disease Spreads"; and for a starter, a funny one about a monkey.

After the movies, when they parted for the night, Mr. Donner said to Padre Sahib, "I know that you will be busy tomorrow preaching in different places. But I hope that after Sunday school in the afternoon, you'll be able to spare Chand and Roshan to come to our house. Some of us want to ask questions about India and about yourselves. So be prepared to tell your life stories."

"And we'll have ice cream," added Mrs. Donner, "and save some for Padre Sahib when he comes back from his preaching."

Chand wondered what he could tell about himself that would prove interesting to Americans. But he did like the idea of having more ice cream.

6: Fireside Stories

The wood fire in the open fireplace glowed cheerfully in the comfortable American room. Several boys and girls and a few grownups were gathered around it when Roshan and Chand came in from teaching new songs at three meetings in different sections. Roshan thought the American friends would like to hear Chand sing, so he had brought along the drums. He and Chand took off their shoes and squatted comfortably on the floor in front of the fire.

First, everybody wanted to learn how to sit "Turk fashion," as they called it. With lots of laughter, they tried to fold their feet properly, and some of them managed very well. Then Roshan began to play the small drums, beating with the heel of his hand on the edges of the tight skin and

tapping the rhythm with the fingers of his other hand. Chand's voice was very clear and true, and he sang "**Ham, Hindi Jawan Hain.**"

They could see, as he sang with his head thrown back and his eyes shining, that it meant a lot to him. And they understood why when Roshan translated.

> *We are the youth of India.*
> *We come to make the world free.*
> *No religion teaches enmity.*
> *We come to build friendship.*
> *We come to work together.*

After the singing, Mrs. Donner served ice cream.

"Now for our questions!" Mr. Donner interrupted the

chatter. "We want to know how many Christians there are in India, and why you are Christians."

Roshan answered, "Christians are a very small part of the population of India. Most of the people are Hindus, but there are also a large number of Muslims, some Jains, and, of course, in the Punjab especially, a great many Sikhs. But the Christian church is growing in numbers and strength. I think that one out of every forty-six persons in India is a Christian. Chand is a third generation Christian. That means that his grandparents were converts from some other religion. I think Padre Gulam Masih is a second generation Christian. For myself, my father was a Sikh who left all for Christ. And I have a college classmate who was a Muslim and has just joined our Christian church. I could tell you stories of all of them, if I had time."

"Tell us about yourself, anyway," asked Mrs. Donner.

They all settled themselves to listen. Chand had never heard the story of Roshan's family, and he tried to understand as much of the English as he could.

Roshan began, "My father's name was Jodh Singh. He was a younger son of a rich Sikh landowner, and when he was a boy he went to a Christian school for a short time. When he grew up, he went into the Indian army as an officer. He married a girl in his own village, and she lived with her mother-in-law and the wives and children of the other brothers. My father was with his family only when on leave from the army.

"He traveled all over India. One day he was in a city in the south when he noticed a Hindu *pundit,* a wise man, coming out of a large house with a beautiful garden. The man looked very learned and holy in his saffron-colored robe. Under his arm he carried a large book that my father recognized as the Bible because it was like the one in the Christian school. My father thought it very curious that this learned Hindu should have a Bible, so he asked him about it.

" 'If you are interested,' said the pundit, 'go into that bungalow. There is a very kind lady there who will answer your questions. I go to her every day to learn about this Holy Book.'

"My father was welcomed by that missionary lady, and she helped him with friendliness and Christian teaching. She gave him a Bible, and he read the story of Jesus' life over and over again. Love for Jesus came into his heart, and he decided to give his life to Christ. He asked the pastor of the church in that city to baptize him, and he became a member of the church.

"This was not an easy decision to make. When boys like you"—the storyteller looked at Mike and Chand—"decide to join the church, perhaps some of your companions laugh and tease you, and maybe you are a little afraid of being thought a goody-goody. You know it will be hard to live a Christian life. But after all, your parents are Christians, and you won't have to leave your family and friends. It was different with my father. When he got his next leave and went back to his village, he told his wife that he was a Christian. She cried and cried and would not listen to his explanations. Then he told his father. The old man was very angry.

" 'You are no longer my son!' he shouted. 'I will give your portion of the harvest and the land to your brothers. I will take care of your wife and the little ones, but you must leave home. I never want to see your face again.'

"Now, that family owned the whole village and many acres of good land around it. So my father gave up great riches for himself and his family when he made the decision. He told my mother about Jesus and wanted her to become a Christian, too, and then they would all go away and start a new life.

"But my mother could not be persuaded to give up her own religion. She was a very good woman, and she believed in the teachings of the Sikh holy book. She loved her husband, but she did not dare to become a Christian.

"My father left his family sadly. He gave up his army career and went to the missionaries in a town fifty miles away and asked their advice and help. At first, he found only day labor to support himself. Later he got a job as sexton of the church, and still later, he became a teacher. Now he is principal of an important Christian high school and a member of the municipal committee of our big city.

"My mother was very lonely without her husband. She and her children had plenty to eat and good clothes. My grandparents gave her about everything she wanted. But she could not be happy. She kept thinking about the wonderful Jesus Christ who had called her husband to follow him. After months of struggle in her heart, she secretly tied up some cooked food in a cloth and planned to leave.

"She would not take anything belonging to the family. My father had left her a few rupees, which she had saved. She wore her poorest clothes and left behind all her jewelry and the children's finery. One day, just as dawn was breaking over the quiet village, she took her four-year-old daughter by the hand, the baby boy on her hip, and walked out of her home, followed by the six-year-old son. I was that baby boy. My brother just barely remembers that terrible, hungry journey.

"Twenty-five miles they walked over rough village roads. Good people helped her on her way. She grew very tired and was often frightened, for she had never been away from home before. My mother is a very strong and determined woman, so she kept on. When she came to the Grand Trunk Road, she hired a cart to take them the rest of the way. The whole journey took nearly a week.

"My father was very happy when his family joined him. He gave us all new names. I was called Roshan, which means 'Light.' We children grew up in a Christian home.

"My mother and father are the best Christians I know. They really live the Christlike life. By scrimping and saving, they sent all three of us to college. My brother is now serving Christ and India as a surgeon. My sister is an inspectress of schools.

"Not long ago, I took my mother and sister back to the old village. The headman, my great-uncle, welcomed us heartily. My sister prepared a big meal, and all the relatives sat down to eat in the house that we had left so many years ago. The relatives ate with us the meal we offered. My mother remembered that in the old days the family could never have taken food from her hands. Now they were welcoming us back, though once they had never wanted to see us again.

" 'Blessings, blessings,' my mother told them. 'Only blessings have I had in my life since we became Christian.'

" 'I believe you,' said my great-uncle. 'Our branch of the family has wealth, but yours has character and honor.' "

As Roshan finished, there was a quiet pause, and then someone said, "Can we hear about Chand's family now?"

But Chand turned suddenly shy. He could not speak to these strange people around him and tell them about his family. Besides, he realized that he did not know too much about how his family became Christians. Though he had heard the story, he had not paid much attention to it.

Roshan saw that Chand was in difficulty. "I wish that you could hear Master Shera tell the story himself," he said. "His family were outcastes before they became Christians. And now Master Shera is an honored teacher. His son, Chand here, is the champion athlete of the district."

"Perhaps we can meet Master Shera some day and hear his story," said Mr. Donner. "Now we must think of tomorrow. Work on the big project has to begin early in

the morning. I like to think that it will bring a better and happier life to a hundred and thirty-five million people. I want to have a share in helping the poor of India."

"*Beshak*," said Mrs. Donner, using a common expression meaning "certainly." She went on. "I do feel sometimes that we are not seeing much of India. Here we are, living American style, in a kind of little America. I wish we could really get out into the villages and see the real India, not just this part where a new industrial life is beginning."

"That gives me an idea," said Roshan. "Mike was telling me how much he would like to learn how to play *kubuddi* and saying that he certainly would like to show his friends in Saginaw—did I say that right?—some of Chand's champion wrestling tricks. Why not let Mike go back with us to Jalalabad? Master Shera and Chand's mother will take excellent care of him, and he'll see a lot of interesting things and add to his collections. After a week, you can go to the village to get him and stay there yourselves for a day or two. Then you will get acquainted with Master Shera, and he can tell you himself the story you missed tonight."

"How would you like that, son?" asked Mr. Donner.

There was no question about Mike's liking the idea. And Chand understood enough to make his eyes shine.

"Mike—come—my—house—my mother—make—bread—curry—"

That was the longest English sentence Chand had ever tried.

"I approve of the plan," said Mr. Donner, and Mrs. Donner agreed. She said, "While Mike is away, I mean to run off for a week and see some sights. Before we go to live in New Delhi in January, I want to see at least one mission hospital and a school and some social work in the villages. So I am going off on a project of my own. I wish you could come along, Jim," she said to Mr. Donner.

"You know, dear," said Mr. Donner, "I just can't get away. If I manage to go with you to visit the Greens at the Central School for three days at Christmas and then take off a few days in the last of January to get settled in New Delhi, it will be all the sight-seeing I can have, I fear."

After they talked a little about what Mike would have to take for his trip, they had evening prayers. Each one spoke a little prayer of thanks for his new Indian friends and asked God's blessing on Roshan and his movies, also for Padre Sahib and his preaching. Then they asked Chand to teach them to sing a Christian hymn.

"A-o, a-o, Yisu pas a-o," sang Chand and Roshan. The tune was catchy, and the sweet drums, soft and loud, helped them to keep the time. It was a good song to close a happy day.

> *Come, come, come to Jesus,*
> *He is calling you now.*
> *Come, come, come to Jesus,*
> *He is calling you now.*

7:   *Village Guest*

Under Roshan's direction, next morning, Mike tied up his bedding roll. He took a small quilt for a mattress, two blankets, and some sheets and towels. Mrs. Donner tucked into his airplane bag, along with his toilet articles, some cans of American food as a special treat for Chand's family. Roshan had suggested tuna fish, canned peaches, and coffee. Then a goodly supply of dried whole milk and egg powder was loaded on the pick-up truck for Master Shera to give to poor people in the village, and bottles and bottles of vitamin pills. Church World Service had sent these to India for Mrs. Donner to give away to those who needed more food. On each bottle of vitamin pills was the label "From the Christians of America to Their Friends Overseas."

On the way home, Roshan and Chand asked Mike a lot of questions about America. Roshan translated to Chand.

"It is wonderful the way America is helping our country," Roshan said. "We are always having famine conditions in some parts of India, and even in the Punjab, which usually sells part of its harvest to more needy districts, hardly any of the working people have really enough to eat. Unless a village family has a goat or a cow, the children are thin and weak and often die of pneumonia or other fevers. But why should rich America care? They have sent us wheat and rice and milk powder and even agricultural tools. Why do they do it?"

"Well, I think we ought to," said Mike hotly. "Why shouldn't we? We surely have enough, and we don't like to think of people starving anywhere in the world. We talked about it once in our church school class, and one of the fellows said it wasn't any of our business if the people in other countries were hungry. Probably they were lazy and didn't work the way we do. Then our teacher gave us quite a talk on what Christians should do to help others."

"America is giving a great deal of help under the Point Four Program," Roshan went on thoughtfully. "These hydroelectric and rural community projects are helping our people to help themselves."

"My father says he wouldn't be interested in this work if it were just a lot of Americans coming out on big salaries to do big things," said Mike. "He says the Indian engineers who work with him are awfully clever fellows.

Some of them haven't had much experience, and the American workers have all had jobs on big river projects at home and really can give good advice and help. But the Indians have the scientific knowledge, all right, and they'll soon take over the whole job."

The truck was rolling along a straight, level road that looked as if it would never end. Just at sunset they pulled into the little village of Jalalabad.

"I have brought you another son, Ustani-ji," called Roshan, giving Kamini the title that meant a woman teacher. "Here is Chand's new American friend, Mike."

Chand soon had a nice room fixed up for Mike right by the schoolroom. It was very tiny, for it was really a little storeroom. It had a small window, and Chand nailed across it a piece of old wire netting as a screen.

"It will keep the flies out," he told Mike. "You won't have to put a mosquito curtain over your bed the way we do."

Chand carried in a bed that was very interesting to Mike. He called it a *charpai*, which means "four legs." The legs were of heavy wood and about twenty inches high. They were held together with a wooden frame on which was woven a close net of heavy cord. Chand pulled the cord very tight so that Mike's quilt and blankets would lie smooth.

Meanwhile, Kamini was putting more lentils and rice on the fire, and Tara was busily patting out five or six more *chapatties*. Roshan had to drive on to another village, but he was sure that he was leaving Mike in good hands.

Mike was glad to find that Master-ji spoke English and even Kamini could say in her gentle voice, "Mike is my son. I am very glad."

Mike had a good night's sleep and was up for a breakfast of bread cakes and milk. Tara was very busy, jumping up to bring brushwood to keep the fire bright.

"Baa, baa," called Nuri in a plaintive voice, and Chand was off to get her a bundle of mustard plants. After breakfast, Mike helped Chand with the chores and watched him milk Sundri, the buffalo.

Master Shera was pleased to see how handy Mike was with the chores.

"I have a calf of my own at home," Mike told him. "I took second prize at the country fair. But I never saw a cow-buffalo like Sundri before. I've just seen the buffalo that are used to pull wagons and plows."

"Come and see our baby deer," said Chand.

The fawn's big, soft eyes looked grateful as it lapped up warm milk Kamini had placed near its basket. Its long legs were wrapped in an old blanket. Chand unwrapped one of them and showed that it was bound up.

"Leg hurt. Papa make well," he said in English.

Mike asked, "Where did you get the baby deer?" But Chand's English was not good enough to explain. When Mike went to Master Shera with his question, Chand wished that he had spent more time on his English primer.

"Ever since I was a boy, I've liked animals," Master

Shera told Mike. "I have had the good fortune to find and help many little beasts that are hurt or lost. One day in the forest I saw this fawn lying under a tree, with its leg caught in a twisted root. Not far away was the poor mother, dead from a hunter's shot. I brought the fawn home, and I hope that its leg will soon be well."

The fawn had no name. Mike named it Bambi. He loved to stroke its soft skin, and he thought that it was a fine pet.

Of course, Mike was shown around the school. He looked carefully at everything so he could tell the boys at home what it was like. The floor was of hard packed dirt, and the walls were mud plastered and whitewashed. There were only two small blackboards, one in each room. Above the line of the blackboards was a frieze painted in water colors in a pretty design of lotus and other flowers. There were a few bright unframed pictures on the walls and two big calendars, one with a picture of Jawaharlal Nehru and the other of Abraham Lincoln. There were charts and small pictures painted by the pupils on pieces of scrap paper.

What interested Mike most were the pictures of animals painted on each pillar between the windows. There was a baby deer that looked like Bambi, a beautiful peacock, a goat and a cow, an elephant and a camel.

"Master Shera is like me," he thought. "He is very fond of animals."

Before school began there was a great hustle and bustle out in the flower garden. Chand had already shown Mike the neat, regular beds of the school garden, where spinach, cauliflower, carrots, and great long radishes were being harvested by the children every day and where peas and tomatoes were looking strong and healthy. They would be ready to eat in February.

In the corners and along the borders of the plots were great masses of sunny marigolds, many colored cosmos, and dark yellow daisies. Among the marigolds the little girls were busy chattering away as they strung the stemless blossoms together to make garlands. They made eight or ten long ones before the school bell rang.

Mike was quite embarrassed when he had to stand with Master-ji and Ustani-ji in front of the whole school assembled in the yard. The forty children were all on time that morning, curious to see the foreign visitor. They stood neatly, by classes. From the Fifth Class row, Chand winked at Mike to encourage him. Then from each row came two children, a boy and a girl, carrying garlands to hang on Mike's neck. Chand showed him by gestures just what to do.

Mike bent his head while each garland was hung on his neck and then said *Namaste* with folded hands. The garlands got heavier and heavier. For the last ones, brought by the kindergarteners, he had to stoop down a long way.

"I hope you don't mind," explained Master-ji. "It is our custom. We are so glad to have you with us, and this is the way we do honor to our guests."

All that day, Chand felt on top of the world. At the very beginning, when they marched in for prayers and stood for the national anthem, he was appointed to call the salute. In his beautiful, strong voice, he gave the yodel-like cry, "*Quami jalana!* Salute the nation!" The other children shouted in reply, "*Jai Hind!* Hail India!"

Mike liked the salute and wanted to learn the song "*Jana, Gana, Mana*" when he heard it sung.

All day long, Chand was teaching his guest something. Mike caught on quickly in the *kubuddi* and *kushti* games, but, of course, he couldn't be as good as Chand in a hurry.

Day by day, Chand was helping Mike to get acquainted. It seemed to him that half the village boys, big and little, were hanging around all the time. Mike appeared to enjoy it and tried to be friendly to all. Chand liked it best when he and Mike played with his own particular friends.

Mike got quite chummy with Yusuf. "That guy certainly is bright," Mike thought. He kept taking home an English First Reader that Master-ji had, and every day he could say a lot of new sentences. He learned English faster than Mike learned Hindustani.

There had always been some rivalry between Chand and Ram. Chand was the son of the teacher and good at sports. Ram was the son of the rich man of the village. He was the only boy in the village to own a bicycle, and he had been to Delhi. Ram was used to being important.

After some days, trouble broke out among the boys. It had been brewing for some time. When Chand became the champion, Ram tried to comfort himself by thinking that Chand couldn't afford to go to Delhi with the scouts. Chand was working Saturday half-holidays to earn money for his fare, but he wouldn't be able to get enough for it this year, while he, Ram, could have nearly everything he wanted just by asking his father.

But when Mike came to be Chand's guest, it was more than Ram could bear. "It's sickening how proud Chand acts about his American guest," he thought. "You'd think he was a Lat Sahib."

Almost unconsciously Ram began to pass mean remarks about the foreigner. Before long, a number of the boys were saying bad words under their breath about the newcomer. Mike couldn't understand the words, but he felt the unfriendly spirit.

Chand understood all right. "Quit your fooling!" he yelled at them angrily. "Stop teasing my friend!"

The boys saw his doubled-up fists and stopped their meanness for a while. Then they started again, snatching away the piece of wood Mike was trying to whittle, losing the nice penknife he lent them, laughing whenever he tried to speak their language.

Chand was getting more and more angry. There would surely be a bad fight soon. Mike didn't want to bring trouble to his friends. Good, clean wrestling was all right, but not this bitter enmity. He wondered whether he could do anything to help.

One day an opportunity came unexpectedly. Mike learned from Chand that Ram's bicycle, of which he was very proud, was out of order. Nobody in the village knew how to repair it, and Ram's father was always forgetting to take it to the city to be fixed.

"I think I could take it apart and repair it," Mike said to Chand. "I'm good at mechanical things. What would you think about that?"

Chand felt a struggle within himself. He'd been rather glad that Ram couldn't show off on his bicycle, as he usually did. And here was Mike suggesting help for Ram.

Mike never knew of Chand's violent inner struggle because in a minute his friend said, "It's a good idea! Let's ask my father about it."

Master Shera agreed and got permission from Ram's father for Mike to take apart the bicycle. Half the boys of

the village gathered on Saturday afternoon to look on as Mike worked carefully on the bicycle. His every move was watched. By the end of the afternoon the bicycle was together again and working.

"*Jai,* Mike!" yelled the boys when Ram jumped on the bicycle and rode it around the village. Ram gave Mike a turn and then Chand.

That evening Ram came to talk to Chand privately. "My father says I must give Mike something for fixing my bicycle, and I, too, want it. But what can I give? Those Americans have everything." Ram looked at Chand expectantly.

Chand knew well enough what Mike would like. But he found it hard to tell the boy who had been his rival about something his new friend would like. Yet he did it, after a little struggle.

"Mike has a collection of old coins. He would like something for that."

Ram jumped at the idea. "My old Victoria rupee! I'll give him that." Ram seemed pleased to be able to give something Mike really wanted. Off he went to get the coin.

Chand found himself liking Ram better than he ever had. Maybe the boy wasn't as mean as he often seemed. The old feeling of rivalry had somehow gone out of Chand.

When Ram brought the old coin, Mike hardly knew how to say his thanks, but he managed to do it by using two languages.

Before he went to bed, Chand said to his father, "Mike can do a lot of things that I can't."

"I expect he works harder in school than you do," said his father.

"Do you think I could be a champion in my studies if I tried?" Chand asked with a little laugh.

"I think so, my son," said Master Shera. "And I am pleased to see that you are learning to win some other kinds of contests besides sports."

This time Chand understood what the words meant, but he was surprised that his father had noticed.

8: Visit from a Cobra

Chand and his family tried hard to make every day interesting for Mike. Mother cooked special dishes so that he would enjoy Indian food. Father tried to find specimens for him to add to his collection. Chand and Tara took him out to the highway to see the caravans of loaded camels go by.

Several times they went over to the well of a neighboring farmer to watch his camel work the big well-wheel. The camel was blindfolded and went steadily round and round without being driven. They collected hairs from the camel's tail and helped Mike to make a real camel-hair brush for painting.

But Mike had expected to find a lot of strange animals in India and so far he had seen only familiar ones.

Chand had given his friend a number of gorgeous peacock feathers, as well as some pretty ones dropped by other bright colored birds. They had seen peacocks flying and roosting in trees, with their tails neatly folded, so that they looked dark gray all over. But never once had the birds spread out their tails. Master Shera said that Mike must see that sight. So one morning he woke the boys up before dawn and took them out to the fields to see the peacocks.

"Lie perfectly still," commanded Master Shera, as they hid in the tall reeds. The light was so dim that they hardly saw the parting of the reeds as a big, dark bird walked toward them in a stately march. He stood still, and quietly there gathered in a small semicircle in front of him six other smaller birds.

"They are the females, the pea-hens," Master Shera whispered. "Watch the cock."

Very, very slowly, the proud peacock spread his gorgeous tailfeathers like a great fan and began a fluttery dance. The rainbow colored fan of feathers stood straight up at his back. Faster and faster he moved. The circle of drab colored birds watched him as if fascinated. There was not a sound. Chand and Mike hardly breathed. The first rays of the dawn filtered through the reeds and lighted up the colors of the peacock's tail.

"I never saw anything so beautiful!" murmured Mike.

At that, the gorgeous tail fan closed slowly. The great bird unfolded his wings and soared into the air. He was followed by the others in a whir of wings.

On the walk home Master Shera told them stories about animals. One of them was about a cobra to whom he had once fed milk when he was a boy. Mike wished he could see a cobra. But Master Shera warned him that Raj Nag, the king cobra, was very dangerous, if you did not understand his habits. However, Mike made up his mind he would see one if he could. Maybe he could even get a cobra skin for his collection.

Mike talked about the cobra to Yusuf, who assured him that there was no danger if you were careful. Together they went to a big pile of old bricks and rubbish, just the place where snakes often live. And there, sure enough, they found a cobra, a baby one, curled up in a hole under some brushwood. They made sure that Mother Cobra was not around anywhere. Then they put over the hole a little clay pot Yusuf had brought. The little cobra slithered into it and curled up in the bottom. When they got back they borrowed a glass bottle from Ram and put the cobra into it. They fed it by pouring a little milk into the bottle. The baby cobra was about ten inches long and looked pretty in the bottle. When it was dark they hid him in Mike's room.

That night after supper Mike went to his room with a lantern, to write in his diary. He closed the door and opened the screened window. He put the bottle with the little cobra on the window sill. How cute he looked curled up, asleep!

Suddenly Mike heard an angry hiss. Outside the little

window, the moonlight shone on the head of a large cobra, with its hood spread, poised to strike.

The snake's head darted quickly forward with a loud bang on the window screen. Again and again it beat on the thin wire netting. Mike was paralyzed with fright. He could not cry out. He could only close his ears with his hands pressed against them to shut out the horrible sharp sound of that quick, regular strike. The window screen was all that saved him. How long would it last?

Then he heard a stealthy sound. Behind the great snake, he saw a boy moving very slowly and carefully toward the schoolyard tree. It was Chand. Without a sound he took down the heavy iron that he rang every day for the school bell. Taking careful aim he hurled it at the cobra's head.

Mike screamed. Master Shera came running and finished off the snake with a club. Shamefaced, Mike showed

him the little snake in the bottle and told what had happened.

"It was the mother cobra, come to find her baby," said Master Shera. "The best place to keep a baby cobra is in alcohol. We can fix him up for your collection. And I'll show you how to skin the big cobra."

"Perhaps your fright will help you to take advice," Master Shera went on rather sternly. "That skin will always remind you that cobras are dangerous."

Then he called the family together for prayers and they thanked God for Mike's safety.

The next day Mike's mother arrived. She could stay only a couple of days, and she wanted to see everything that Tara and Chand and Mike had to show her. She was eager to learn to cook some of the Indian dishes Mike liked so well. Kamini promised to let her help prepare the evening meal.

As soon as he could, without being impolite, Mike took his mother away for a little walk around the village. He had so many things to tell her, about the peacocks and Ram's bicycle, and especially about Chand.

"You wouldn't believe it, Mother, but that guy is working hard every Saturday afternoon to earn a few annas for his travel fund. The scouts are going to Delhi for Republic Day. Chand wants to go so much, but it will cost eighteen rupees. He doesn't have that much, and he just can't earn enough. The best he can make, saving his tournament prize and his earnings, is about eleven rupees. All he needs is about a dollar and a half. I sure wanted to give it to him, but I was afraid I'd hurt his feelings. But can't we do something about it, Mother?"

"You were right not to give it to him, son, lest you hurt his pride. We must think of some friendly way to help him get the trip to Delhi. Would Tara like to go, too, do you think?"

"Oh, Mother, she's crazy about traveling, too. But she wants Chand to go, and she's working to help him. Oh, please fix it up for them!"

Mrs. Donner promised to think over the problem during her visit. She spent the afternoon with Kamini. A number of Christian women came in to visit, and Mrs. Donner enjoyed laughing and talking with them. A young bride came to show off her pretty flowered *kurta* and pink satin *sulwar*, and her gilt and silver jewelry.

One neighbor brought in a piece of mutton, as a gift to

the visitor. Kamini cut it into pieces and put it on to boil. When it was tender she fried it with onions and spices which Tara had ground and mixed in a little stone mortar and pestle. The family could afford rice only once a week and Kamini chose this day to cook it, all fluffy and white.

The evening meal was to be a very special one. Chand and Mike came by the stove every few minutes to sniff the good odors that arose from the cooking.

Lentils had been put on to cook earlier in the afternoon in a round copper pot. When they were soft, Kamini seasoned them with salt and plenty of red peppers. When the meal was almost ready, she began to bake the cakes called *chapatties*. The bread mixture had been made earlier. It had taken Kamini almost an hour to mix the wheat flour with salt and water and knead it with her strong hands until it was very light and fine. Now the iron baking plate was put on the small brick fireplace. Tara and her mother made the thin round cakes by picking up a bit of dough and patting it between their hands until it was very thin. On the hot iron it baked dry and puffy and tasted, oh, so good!

Mike was used to the curries that were hot with pepper and spices, and he liked them very much, although the flavors were very different from American food. Mrs. Donner declared that she intended to try cooking more Indian food when she got home.

After the meal Mrs. Donner told Master Shera about the interesting trip she had just taken. She had gone out to a camp in a village where a missionary and his helpers were showing the farmers how to get better seed, giving out medicines for sore eyes and infected wounds, teaching the people how to fight tuberculosis, smallpox, and cholera, and telling them the gospel of Jesus. She had been to the opening ceremony of a beautiful new mission hospital. That hospital had been healing the sick for seventy-five years in old buildings, with poor equipment. Now, many people in the churches in America had given gifts to help the doctors and nurses to heal more people than ever before.

"I owe my life to mission medical work," said Master Shera, "and my education to mission schools."

"Do tell me about it," begged Mrs. Donner.

Chand listened to his father talking to Mrs. Donner and Mike. He could not understand enough English to follow all the conversation, but he knew very well the story his father was telling because he had heard it many times.

First, Master Shera told about the time when he was a poor herdboy, watching a *kubuddi* game and wishing he could go to school. But he was not allowed in the village school, because he was an outcaste, and the other boys would have nothing to do with him. Chand could hardly understand what being an outcaste meant, but he knew the joy that had filled the heart of that long-ago boy when his family became Christians. Then the boy went to the school at Moga and learned much. At first he was lonely without his goat, but by and by he got another goat. Oh, yes, Chand had heard that story many times. And he knew that the boy Shera had done very well in school, so that he was graduated and trained to be a teacher.

It was while he was a teacher in the mission boarding school that the sad part of the story came. Chand himself could almost remember this part because it had happened when Tara was a baby. Father had become very, very sick. He had to go far away to Madar Sanatorium, to be cured of tuberculosis. After he had been cured, they all came to Jalalabad to look after the Christian school and do other work for the village. Father always said that all through those three weary years of sickness, he knew very surely that God would help him to get well. He and his wife promised God that they would give their lives in service to the village people. Chand knew that his father had helped the village in many ways, not only by teaching in the school, but in building up friendship, in teaching people how to prevent diseases like tuberculosis and malaria, and in helping them improve their land and their crops.

"Thank you," said Mrs. Donner when Master Shera had finished. "Would you mind if I tell your story to people at home?"

After the story they all went to bed. Mrs. Donner said that she wanted to visit the school the next day.

In the morning something unusual happened. Rani brought two new children to school. They were thin and dirty and dressed in rags.

"Ustani-ji," she said eagerly to Chand's mother, "I

found these two little boys sitting in the road outside our village. They said they wanted to go to school."

"Thank you, Rani," said Ustani-ji. "It is kind of you to think of these little ones. They look as if no one cares for them. They must belong to one of the refugee families from Pakistan."

She turned to Mrs. Donner and said, "So many Hindu and Sikh families lost their homes and possessions at the time the country was divided. They fled across the border to safety, but they still have no settled homes. In Pakistan it is the same, except that there it is the Muslim families who fled from India and who are without homes."

"It is hard on the children," said Mrs. Donner.

"I know where this family lives," said Indar, who had come up. "They have built a shack out of brushwood and old oil tins against the outer wall of the village. They have no land and the father cannot find work. I think they must be very hungry."

By this time, the two little boys were playing in the schoolyard with the other children. But when the classes started to go into school, the older one held back.

"Our clothes are not right," he told Rani. "When we used to go to school in our city, our mother always put clean clothes on us."

Prem stepped up to the teacher.

"Master-ji," he suggested, "if you will, in your kindness, give permission, I can run home and get a clean shirt for this older boy."

Vijai and another Hindu boy broke in eagerly, saying they would bring pants for both and a shirt for the younger one. Chand and Yusuf took the two boys to the well for a bath.

While they were gone, the other children held a meeting. It was time for opening prayers, but they all thought this was a good time to worship God by giving help.

The first idea was to give the newcomers something to eat. Ruth and Rani were appointed to help Ustani-ji bake some *chapatties*. Moti offered to build the fire for them.

"Probably they will come to school hungry every day," said Rani thoughtfully.

Tara had kept quiet up till then. She knew her mother had given away almost all the cans of milk and eggs Mrs. Donner had sent with Mike. There were so many poor people around. She began figuring on her slate.

"I have an idea," she said suddenly.

The others all listened, for Tara was always very good at making plans.

"First of all," she said, "I would suggest that the Christian children here give the boys one hot meal a day."

"If you do that," said Indar, "we Sikhs will give them warm coats for the winter."

"Good!" said Master-ji. "And how would you Hindu boys and girls like to buy their schoolbooks and slates?"

All agreed eagerly. "But what is your plan for the food, Tara?" asked Ruth, who knew that many of the Christian families were often hungry themselves.

"Well," said Tara importantly, showing her slate, "here is a list of all the Christian families that have a milk-giving animal. There are just twelve. Some have a buffalo, one has a cow, and the rest have goats. Now, if each one of you boys and girls will bring a pint of milk on one school day in two weeks, the boys can each have one cup of milk a day. Then all the rest choose a day and bring a handful of flour on that day. That will give the boys bread each day. I will help Mother bake the bread. We'll cook vegetables from the school garden for them, and Mother can cook a little of the egg powder that came from America."

The children agreed with pleasure because all of them knew what it was to be hungry. For some of them the plan meant giving up their own drink of milk on the day of their turn. Tara decided to give up her buffalo milk, which she liked, and drink goat's milk, which she hated. Tara was made chairman of the food committee, and she made a chart to hang on the wall, to remind everyone.

Mrs. Donner said to Chand that evening, "Mike and I have something more to tell our church people back home."

Next morning Mrs. Donner and Mike had to go. Before she left, Mrs. Donner wanted to hear the national anthem sung by the school. Chand called for the salute, and all the children shouted, *"Jai Hind!* Hail India!" Then they sang *"Jana, Gana, Mana."* Master-ji pointed out on the wall map all the different places and regions mentioned in the first verse.

The second verse called all the pople of India to serve their country.

"Hindus, Buddhists, Sikhs, Jains," they sang.

"Muslims, Christians—"

"It seems to me," said Mike thoughtfully to his mother, "that this country and my country are a lot alike. So many different kinds of people in the United States are learning to be good Americans, and so many different kinds of people in India are learning to be good citizens."

Mike was hoping his mother would say something about Chand's trip to Delhi. But when he asked her, she only smiled and said, "I have a plan."

Just before leaving, she announced, "I have a surprise for you. The Donner family are invited to spend Christmas with the Greens at the Central School, and Mr. Green is going to ask Master Shera, Kamini, Chand, and Tara to come over for a visit so that we can hear Indian Christmas carols sung in the best manner. So we'll all be together soon again. Good by! We'll be seeing you."

Chand and Tara counted the days ahead. They could hardly wait for Christmas to come.

9: Surprises

It was the week before Christmas at Jalalabad School. Preparations for Great Day, as the festival was called, had been going on for almost a month. Chand and Tara and their friends had been busy every minute. Yards and yards of paper chains had been made by the younger children from strips of paper cut from the colored advertising pages of magazines Mrs. Green had given Ustani-ji. The older boys and girls cut out pretty pictures from the same magazines and pasted paper frames on them. Ustani-ji was kept busy making paste.

Chand had taught the boys and girls some new Christmas carols which they could now sing very well. He had helped the first graders to make stars and had finished the wings for the angels in the school play.

Tara and Ruth had made crowns for two of the Wise Men in the Fourth Class drama. They planned to dress the third Wise Man in a saffron colored robe, like a Hindu holy man.

"The Bible calls them Wise Men from the East, and India is in the East," argued Ruth.

"Yes," agreed Ustani-ji, "and so many Indians through all the ages have searched for God that it is not hard to think that one of our Wise Men may have seen the star."

The schoolchildren had not forgotten Mike and his mother. They had made Christmas gifts for them—two books full of lovely pictures. Some of the pictures were drawn by the teacher and colored by the pupils. Some were painted in water colors by the best artists in the different classes. Other boys and girls wrote in descriptions and poems in beautiful Hindi writing. These Mr. Green would translate into English, so that Mike could understand them. Mrs. Donner's book was on "Our Homes," and it showed how a village house is built, how a *charpai* is made, and what things the mothers use in their kitchens for cooking the food. Mike's book was on "Our Animals."

Chand and his father had a soft piece of deerskin which they had prepared for Mike's Christmas present.

In the midst of all the preparations there came a letter from Mike begging Chand to come to the Greens a day ahead of his family, so that they could have some time together. "We have to leave right after Christmas," Mike wrote, "and I want to see you."

Chand wished to do very much as Mike asked, but it meant that he would miss the Christmas festival at Jalalabad.

"I don't see how you can bear to miss our entertainment," Tara said unhappily. "I am to be Mary in the drama, and if you go, you won't even see me."

Chand was worried about the Christmas chorus and the play. "I think I'd better stay here until after the festival," he said to his father. "There is a lot for me to do."

Master Shera was pleased to see that his son was thinking of others besides himself. He said to his family, "I think that Chand should do as Mike asks. They may never have a chance to be together again after this Christmas. Let him leave a day ahead of us. I will look after his duties."

So the second day before Christmas, Chand started very early for Central School. He marched off with his bedding roll on his head. Inside it was the gift for Mike. He was to walk to the main road, where Mr. Green would pick him up as he returned from a tour.

As Chand strode along, his thoughts were back at the school and its plans for Christmas. His class had made a large poster illustrating the word *Prem*—friendship. Near the top was the verse the angels sang, done in beautiful Hindi lettering, "Glory to God in the highest, and on earth peace among men."

The border was a design of small world globes. Near the bottom was a picture of children joining hands

around the globe. At the festival several of the pupils were
going to tell stories of Christmas in other lands and Yusuf
was to read his essay on "Friends."

One of the questions Chand meant to ask Mike was
about those other countries. How many of them had he
seen? England? Holland? France? Germany? Italy? Egypt?
Would he see the Philippines and Japan on the way back
to America?

"And I haven't even seen Delhi!" Chand thought as he
walked through the fields in the cold, clear morning air.

The sun was just peeping up over the horizon, making
a path of light stretching straight and far ahead of him.
On both sides there was nothing to be seen but fields of
green wheat, checkered with great patches of bright
yellow mustard flowers. It seemed to Chand as if he could
walk on forever, right into the sunrise.

Soon after Chand reached the highroad, Mr. Green
drove up in his station wagon. It was full of young men

who were on their way from their village to attend a *Prem Bhojan,* Friendship Feast, with the Christians at Padre Sahib's village.

When they arrived at the village, they found Padre Sahib looking troubled.

"The wife of Sundar, one of the elders of this church, is seriously ill with pneumonia. Could you spare a few minutes to come and see her?" he asked.

"Certainly," said Mr. Green.

"Have you had a doctor for her?" he asked, as he looked down at the sick woman, struggling for breath. Three or four small children crowded around crying for their mother.

"I have tried twice to get the doctor from the government dispensary in the next village four miles away, but he won't make the trip," Padre Sahib told him.

"I'll take her to the mission hospital in the pickup," said Mr. Green. "I think they will have some penicillin for her." With the help of Chand and Padre Sahib, he moved the patient into the back seat of his car and made room for her husband and her mother.

Ten miles farther on, a dignified looking Hindu came out into the road to hail them. Mr. Green told Chand that he was a friend whom he had helped in efforts to improve his village. The man told them that his son, who was in his last year at college, was sick and suffering great pain. The village *hakim* was with him and a young doctor trained in Western medicine, but they could not help him. The young doctor had said that the son had appendicitis and advised an immediate operation at the mission hospital.

"Please, can you take him to the hospital?" the Hindu begged. "I have no way of getting him there."

"I'm thankful I have a station wagon instead of a jeep," said Mr. Green, as the second patient with his mother and aunt and father was helped into the car.

The big city where the mission hospital was located was ten miles beyond the Central School. By the time Mr. Green had the sick people settled under the care of the missionary doctor, it was nearly noon. The Hindu college boy was to have an emergency operation, and the first penicillin injection had been given to the mother of the Christian family. Mr. Green said he would come back the next day to see how they were getting on and drove to his home.

Mike was waiting impatiently for his friend. "I thought you would never get here," he said. "Come on. Mr. Green says I'm to show you around the school, and he'll come with us to translate."

Chand had never been to the Central School before. He looked at the fine new buildings, the big farm, and the interesting workshops. This was where Yusuf would be coming next year. How about himself? Where would he be? Perhaps there were more interesting things to do than being a wrestling champion.

Mike showed him some boys working at wiring the new

buildings for electricity. "They learn such useful things here," he said. "It is something like our junior high in my home town."

"But the boys have to work awful hard," objected Chand. "It is not like other schools where they just learn to be scholars."

"Well, I think it is good for educated people to know how to do practical things," suggested Mike.

"I know," said Chand grinning. "My father is always telling me a Punjabi proverb—'My son knows how to comb his hair, but he does not know how to comb the earth.'"

Mr. Green thought this a good time for a surprise.

"I got an airmail letter yesterday. A church school in America has promised $3.00 a month for the support of a Christian boy in Central School. Would you like to come next term, Chand? Your father will have to pay only about five rupees, besides your clothes and travel, of course, and by your work you could earn five rupees more."

Chand hesitated. He felt surprised and grateful, yet he was not ready to make up his mind. "I'll have to talk it over with my father," he said. "How did that church school class come to know about our school?"

Mike turned away his head to hide a smile. "That letter I wrote to my church school about my champion friend must have been a good one," he thought. To Chand he said, "Central School will be getting a good wrestler if you come."

As soon as he could, Mike dragged Chand over to the farm buildings to see the animals. Chand was much excited over Ferdinand, a Jersey bull that had come all the way from the United States. It had been given by a farmer who wanted to help the Christian school start a good dairy. The boys were told that even the best Indian cow gave less than one-sixth as much milk per day as the average American cow.

"No wonder that millions of Indian boys and girls never even taste milk," said Mike.

In the late afternoon Mrs. Donner helped Mrs. Green and her three children to decorate the house for Christmas. Mike and Chand brought in big pots of poinsettias and some long feathery fronds of a tree that looked a little like an evergreen. Then they went off to the nearby canal to bring some clay that they mixed and kneaded ready for Mrs. Green to model. She made tiny figures of shepherds and sheep and Wise Men, the manger and the Madonna and Baby Jesus, and set up the scene on the mantlepiece. The children made paper chains and twists of red and green tissue paper to festoon the walls.

At bedtime Mike was talking things over with his mother.

"It doesn't seem much like Christmas yet," he said. "I sure do miss the Christmas decorations in the stores and all the Christmas toys and fun, and the—I don't know—the air of Christmas, sort of—"

"Yes," agreed Mrs. Donner, "the church bells and the

cheery greetings and the atmosphere of good will. I never
realized how hard it would be to have to make Christmas
in another country."

"So few people here know about Christmas," sighed
Mike.   . . . . .

> *In the bazaar*
> *Who hears the story?*
> *Who sees his star?*
>
> . . . . .
>
> *Down all these alleys*
> *This Christmas morn*
> *Still no one knows that*
> *A Saviour is born!* [1]

Mrs. Green quoted softly some words of a Christmas
poem from India she had just learned.

Next day they cut and brought in the Christmas tree. It
was just three or four branches of a big tree called *firash,*
which is like the Australian pine. The needles are gray-
green, and they get dry and dusty-looking very quickly.
But after the branches were tied together and set up in a
tub, and the tree draped with tinsel loops, paper chains,
gilded walnut shells, and sparkling bits of glass bangles, it
really made a brave show. Chand thought it was wonderful. Mike kept his opinion of it to himself, for he didn't

---

[1] From the poem "Christmas Outside an Indian Village," by Ruth A. Merrill,
in *Women and Missions* (now *Outreach*), December, 1932, p. 304. Used by
permission.

want to hurt Chand's feelings. Late that afternoon Chand's parents and sister arrived. They were soon busy with the last preparations.

Mrs. Green was especially glad to have Kamini's help in making up packages for nearby poor families. They put pretty pieces of cotton cloth, warm sweaters, balls, and a few toys in each one. There were thirty-five Christmas bundles in all, each wrapped in pink tissue paper.

Christmas morning was exciting. Chand and Mike were startled out of a sound sleep by firecrackers, followed by the voices of schoolboys singing, "King Jesus has come! King Jesus has come!"

The whole household got up, though it was barely light. A big fire was lit and the boys were invited inside. They stood near the fire, shivering in their thin blankets, but still singing. As they got warmer, the singing became more lively. Some of the songs were translations of Western carols that Mike knew and could sing in English, but others were new to him with catchy Indian tunes he wanted to learn.

After a while Mrs. Green came in with a large basket of oranges and a huge trayful of peanuts. Chand and Mike helped distribute them to the boys who left after singing one last carol.

Then came the excitement of opening the Christmas stockings for everyone. They were filled with oranges and peanuts and homemade candy. After breakfast, the household helpers and their families were called in. The cook and the gardener and the old nurse, with all their children and grandchildren, made quite a happy company. They all sang Christmas hymns together and Mr. Donner read the Christmas story from the Hindi Bible and then marched in to see the tree. The Green children gave out the packages that Mrs. Green had made ready. Mike gave out oranges and peanuts and handfuls of hard candy till his arms ached.

After the families went away, the children began to look at their own gifts. That was a jolly, happy time. Mike and Mrs. Donner were delighted with their books. Under the tree was a pretty teapot for Kamini and a book of

Bible stories for Master-ji. And at the very last was the biggest surprise.

"I just found a letter hidden in the branches of the Christmas tree," announced Mr. Green in a loud voice. "It is addressed to Sri and Srimati Shera, Chand, and Tara."

After it was opened, Mr. Donner read it aloud and Mr. Green translated.

"Christmas gift for the Sher Singh family from the Donners—railway fares to Delhi and return. Tara and her mother are invited to stay with us in our apartment in New Delhi, and Master-ji and Chand are to come to us also after the scout meeting is over. We want them to stay two days after Republic Day."

Chand was dazed. He could hardly believe his ears. Mike woke him from his stupor by slapping him on the back and shouting, "Hey, aren't you the fellow who wants to see Delhi?"

10: Delhi at Last

After Christmas, time passed very slowly for Chand and Tara. But at last January was nearly over. In the late afternoon of January 25th, the day before Republic Day, Master Shera started off from Jalalabad with ten happy Boy Scouts, each carrying a neatly rolled blanket on his shoulder and a bundle of food in his hand. Chand was assigned the duty of looking after his mother and sister, who followed the marching troop. They all walked to the highroad, where they took a bus to the railroad station of the city.

The station was dim and dark by the time the Delhi train drew in. A noisy crowd jostled them as they looked in the doors of one after another of the long separate compartments that made up the train. Each one was filled with pushing, struggling people. At last they found one third class compartment with only five or six people in it. They crowded in and found seats on the long wooden benches. Some of the boys climbed to the shelves above, where they could stretch out and and go to sleep. Some put their bedding rolls on the floor and slept there. The place was packed like a can of sardines.

Chand and Tara and the scouts were awake long before six in the morning. They had their bedding neatly rolled and tied when the train pulled into the huge railway station at Delhi. Chand could see from the window at least a dozen gleaming tracks, and several big trains shrieked by while they were getting off the train. With the crowd, they moved down the long, long platform, up the steps of the overhead bridge, down and out of the great iron gate. Each gave up his ticket to the guard who stood at the narrow opening.

"Delhi—at last!" said Chand and Tara together, as they went out of the station.

The brilliant sunshine showed a great open space where scores of taxis and *tongas* stood waiting for passengers. Coolies loaded with trunks and bedding rolls pushed past them. Everyone seemed to know just where to go and how to get there.

Master Shera led his party some distance to a bus stand. It was fun to ride in the bus through the crowded city streets. Tara had never seen so many shops in her life as those that lined both sides of the streets.

Soon they came to the great meadow outside the Old Fort, where the Jalalabad scouts were to camp with a hundred or more other patrols. Behind the camping ground loomed huge walls built of ancient rose-red blocks of sandstone. Parts of them were four hundred years old, Ram said.

While Master-ji and the scouts were picking out their campsite, Mrs. Donner and Mike appeared, having driven in from New Delhi. Tara and her mother went off with them, waving good-by, hoping to see Chand and Father in the parade that afternoon.

There was great activity in the big meadow near the Old Fort Gateway as all the patrols of the Bharat Scouts hurried about, setting up bamboo poles and pieces of canvas for their shelters, spreading their rugs and blankets neatly on the hard ground, putting up forked sticks for hanging their cooking pots, cooking their food, and arranging for sanitation.

After Master Shera's patrol had eaten and washed, they left their camp tidy and set off to do honor to the memory of Mahatma Gandhi, one of India's great leaders who died a few years ago. It was a long walk to the memorial that lay in a quiet spot near the bank of the Jumna River, where the body of the martyred Gandhi had been burned according to Hindu custom. On the walk, Master-ji reminded them of the brave life Gandhi had lived and of how he had suffered imprisonment to win the freedom of India.

"The independence of our nation was won without a war. Our great leader taught us to love peace," he explained.

Every day crowds of people who honor Gandhi go to lay flowers at his memorial. The boys from Jalalabad mounted the memorial, a square of cement set in a simple field of green lawn. It was not like a royal tomb. No decorations or monument were there. But the great piles of many colored flower petals, the wreaths, and the garlands showed the love of the people for him. Reverently the boys placed there the marigolds they had brought from their own school garden. In their hearts was a wish to be good, loyal citizens of the New India, as Mahatma Gandhi had taught.

Their station for the parade in New Delhi was on the broad avenue leading out from the president's house. Almost in front of them were great fountains, throwing up clouds of rainbow-colored spray lighted by hundreds of electric bulbs. Chand noticed that along this avenue, and along many other streets they had marched through, the lovely trees were wired for colored lights.

Beyond the fountains they could see some of the stately, beautiful government buildings where the procession would start. On top of the domes of the Secretariat and the great circular Parliament House, the bronze models of the Lion Capital gleamed in the dazzling sunshine. Master-ji told them that the British rulers had built this new city and had placed on the summits of the build-

ings bronze crowns as symbols of the British Empire. When India became an independent republic within the Commonwealth of Nations, these crowns were taken down and placed in the museum and the Lion Capital was put in their places.

Chand had many times read the story of this beautiful symbol. The Lion Capital is a carved statue of four lions which stood at the top of one of the polished stone pillars set up by King Asoka. Beneath the lions is a band of carving showing four animals and four, twelve-spoked wheels. These wheels form the design for the wheel in the center of the Indian flag.

None of the great stories of Indian history was more thrilling to Chand than that of King Asoka, a young man who turned his kingdom upside down because of a strange and wonderful idea. In all world history, no other great emperor has ever tried to do what Asoka did—give up war. Although he reigned more than 2000 years ago, a great deal is known about his kingdom and his laws because he had many stone pillars carved with messages to his people. He was ruler over the greater part of India when he decided to do away with war. For the rest of his reign he would not allow his soldiers to fight and kill, and there was peace in all his land. To the people of India, the wheel on their flag stands for peace and justice.

Promptly at five o'clock the procession started. In a stately carriage drawn by horses sat the president. He was simply dressed and wore a white Gandhi cap. With folded hands, he greeted the people, bowing to right and left. His face shone with friendliness, wisdom, and patience.

Great cheers arose from the closely packed crowds. Flags waved. The lights came on. Everywhere the trees blossomed in bright colors. That night as the boys marched to their camp, New Delhi and Old Delhi looked like fairyland. Lights outlined the public buildings, the gates of the Old Fort, the great round Parliament House, the post offices, and the foreign embassies.

Later the boys sat around their campfire a while before going to bed. It was a time to feel proud of India. In the few years since she had won the long struggle for independence, the nation had made great progress. It was good to remember the centuries of history behind this new republic. Chand knew that India was, next to China, the oldest civilized country of the world.

Next morning Master Shera arranged for another scoutmaster to look after the Jalalabad group on their return trip. He and Chand found their way to the Donners' apartment in New Delhi. They knew that a sightseeing tour had been planned.

The first place they visited was the Kutb Minar, one of the world's most perfect towers, which they climbed. From its top, they could see scattered all over the plain of Delhi piles of ruins of ancient times. Nearby were a few broken walls of the Red Fort, which was India's capital for two centuries before the Old Fort was built.

Next they went to see the grand halls and palaces built by the Mogul Emperor, Shah Jahan.

"But I thought Shah Jahan lived at Agra," said Mrs. Donner. "We went there when we first arrived in India and saw the palaces and fort and the Taj Mahal, the most beautiful building in all the world."

"Yes," replied Master-ji, "Shah Jahan lived in Agra after his wife's death, and built the Taj Mahal in her memory. But for the first twenty-five years of his long reign, he made Delhi his capital. He was one of the most wonderful builders of all history."

When they saw the halls and mosques and gardens beyond the red gateway, they thought so, too. Every curve of the graceful arches was outlined in lovely colors. Every pillar was inlaid with mosaic pictures of flowers made of precious stones.

Their next call was at a strange-looking place called Jantar Mantar. It is a very interesting observatory built about two hundred years ago. It has some wonderful sun dials and odd shaped marble pillars, steps, and wheels that measure shadows at different seasons and the position of the moon and stars. It was clear that learned men of India knew a great deal about the science of astronomy long before any Western observatory was built. They were good mathematicians, too, long before Columbus discovered America.

Mike was keen to show Chand every single interesting thing in Delhi, but, of course, that was impossible in two days. That night, he begged his mother to invite the visitors to stay another day. Mrs. Donner was glad to do that.

"On the 29th," she told them, "there is to be a very interesting meeting for children only. The Prime Minister, Pundit Jawaharlal Nehru, is going to talk to the children. Tickets are necessary. I am trying hard to get tickets for Tara, Chand, and Mike."

"Oh, that would be great!" said Mike enthusiastically. Chand thought it would be the biggest event of his life if he could see Jawaharlal Nehru and perhaps even shake hands with him.

This plan gave Chand and Mike a whole extra day together. They spent it traveling all over Old Delhi and New Delhi. They wound in and out of the traffic in the crowded lanes of the city, dodging ox carts, hand carts, bicycles, and huge bulls. The sacred bulls wandered at their own sweet will among the open-air shops, munching on the vegetables they took from the stalls. Nobody drove them off, and the motor cars had to detour around them.

At noon the boys sat down on the grass of a park and ate the lunch Mrs. Donner had given them. Chand had something special to tell Mike.

"Next term I go," he stammered out in English, "I go Central School — I read — high school — university — be engineer."

"*Shabash!*" Mike clapped him on the shoulder, highly approving.

On the way back toward Old Delhi late that afternoon they wandered through a village of refugees. Just as they came into a small open space among the crowded huts, a woman screamed wildly. She was standing by an open well. Wringing her hands, she sobbed out that her child had just fallen into the well. Chand understood, though Mike didn't. In a flash, Chand had jumped the low wall and was climbing hand over hand down the well-rope. He knew just what to do, for he had seen such rescues before. In a minute or two, he was coming up again with the small girl over his shoulder.

By this time, many men had gathered, and willing hands were helping him. They laid the child on the ground. Then Mike had his turn. Kneeling by the child, he began to use the new method of saving a drowned person, which he had learned in first aid. Chand pushed the crowd back and comforted the mother.

In a very few minutes, a doctor arrived and took charge. A Delhi policeman took down the boys' names.

When the little girl was breathing properly, the doctor told the mother to put her to bed and keep her warm. Then he turned to the two boys.

"Your prompt action saved that child's life," he said.

"You both knew exactly what to do and did it quickly and efficiently. I shall turn in a full report about this to the government."

It was getting late, so they hurried toward home. They managed to slip in unnoticed. Chand's clothes, though dry now, were somewhat soiled. Mike loaned him clean pants and a shirt to wear.

The friend had been trying to get the tickets Mrs.

Donner wanted for the children's meeting the next day. But so far, he had not succeeded. This was a great disappointment to Mike and Chand. They went to bed never dreaming what a wonderful thing was going to happen the next day.

About ten o'clock in the morning, a messenger in a government uniform arrived with an envelope marked with the government of India seal. It was addressed to Sri Chand, son of Shera, and Mr. Michael Donner. Inside was a short paragraph stating that the Prime Minister had been informed that the two boys had rescued a child who had fallen into a well. In recognition of this act of service, the Prime Minister wished to meet the boys personally. Enclosed were two tickets to the children's meeting that afternoon.

Just before they were ready to start, a friend rushed in with a ticket for Tara, which her father had been able to get.

That afternoon the meeting was held in a large hall. Mike and Chand were given seats in the front row. Tara got a good seat, too, but farther back. All three children would remember that meeting and Pundit Jawaharlal Nehru's speech all their lives.

Pundit Jawaharlal Nehru looked very tired when he first came in. But he soon brightened up and seemed to enjoy talking to the boys and girls. You could see from his face that he really liked children. He began by telling them how to be good citizens. He said that to build democracy in India, every man and woman, boy and girl, had to have a new spirit, and be willing to work hard and work together. He told them about his visits to the United States, Canada, England, Japan, and other countries.

"I found the children in those countries very much like the children here, and so I easily made friends with them. Whenever I had the chance, I played with them a little. That was much more interesting than many of my talks with the grownups. For children everywhere are very much the same. It is the grownups who imagine themselves different and make themselves so.

"We should remember that everywhere there are children like you, going to school and working and playing, and sometimes quarrelling, but always making friends again. You can read about those other countries in your books, and when you grow up many of you will visit them. Go there as friends, and you will find friends to meet you."

Then he looked right into the faces of Chand and Mike.

"Here are two friends," he said, pulling them up to stand on the platform, "citizens of two friendly nations. Yesterday, working together, they saved the life of a child."

Then he shook hands with the two boys.

Chand's eyes were shining as he looked into the face of his country's great leader.

"Tell me, young man," asked Mr. Nehru, speaking in Chand's own language, "what do you mean to do when you grow up?"

Chand gulped down the lump in his throat and spoke up bravely.

"I want to be a good Christian engineer and work for India."

A-o, a-o, Yisu pas-a-o (ah-oh ah-oh yih-soo pas-ah-oh), come, come, come to Jesus

Agra (ah-grah), a city in India where the Taj Mahal is located

Amritsar (ahm-rit-ser), a city in the Punjab

anna (ahn-nah), a copper coin worth 1¼ cents

Asoka (ah-soh-kah), emperor of India around 250 B. C.

bahut accha (buh-hut uh-chah), very good

barra (buh-ruh), big

beshak (beh-shahk), certainly

Bhakra (buh-kruh), a dam in northern India

Bharat (buh-ruht), Hindu name for India

Bulbul (bool-bool), a songbird

Chand (chahnd), a boy's name meaning moon or silver

chapatties (chah-pah-tees), bread made from fine whole wheat flour, water and salt, patted into a thin cake, and baked

charpai (char-pie), a bed

diwa (dee-vah), a small clay lamp

Diwali (dee-vah-lee), a Hindu festival—the Feast of Lights

firash (fee-rahsh), a tree similar to the Australian pine

Gandhi (gahn-dee), famous leader of India

Ganges (gahn-jeez), a river

ghi (ghee), butter

Gulam Masih (goo-lahm mah-see), the pastor in the story

hakim (hah-keem), a village physician

Ham Hindi Jawan Hain (huhm hin-dee jah-vahn high), we are Indian youth

Indar (in-dahr), name of a Hindu god

Jai Hind (jie hihnd), hail, India

Jalalabad (jah-lah-lah-bahd), a village

Jana, Gana, Mana (jah-nah gah-nah mah-nah), go, sing, obey

Jantar Mantar (juhn-tuhr muhn-tuhr), an observatory in Delhi
Jawaharlal Nehru (jah-vah-hahr-lahl nay-roo), Prime Minister
ji (jee), a syllable added to a person's name to show respect
Jodh Singh (jode sing), a man's full name
Jumna (joom-nuh), a river
Kamini (kah-mih-nee), a woman's name
kichri (kitch-ree), rice and peas
kubuddi (kuh-buh-dee), a game
kurta (koor-tah), a long, shirtlike smock
kushti (kush-tee), a wrestling game
Kutb Minar (koo-tub min-ahr), a tower near Delhi
Lahore (lah-hoar), a city in Pakistan, northwest of Delhi
Lali (lah-lee), a pet name meaning red
Lat Sahib (laht sah-hib), the Lord Sahib, any former viceroy
Madar (mah-dahr), a mission tuberculosis hospital
Maya (mah-yah), a girl's name
memsahiba (mehm-sah-hiba), a married woman
Moga (moh-gah), a town in the Punjab
Moti (moh-tee), a boy's name meaning pearl
Namaste (nuh-muhs-teh), a greeting
Nangal (nuhn-guhl), the name of a system of canals
Nuri (noo-ree), a pet name
Padre Sahib (pah-dray sah-hib), a Christian minister or preacher
pahar (pah-hahr), mountain
pani (pah-nee), water
pice (pies), a copper coin, four of which equal an anna
Prem (praym), a boy's name meaning friendship
Prem Bhojan (praym bow-juhn), Friendship Feast
pundit (puhn-dit), a learned man
Punjab (puhn-jahb), a state of northern India
Punjabi (puhn-jah-bee), language spoken in the Punjab
Quami jalana (cow-mee jah-lah-nah), salute the nation

Raj Nag (rahj nahg), king cobra
Ram (rahm), name of a Hindu god
Rampur (rahm-poor), a little village
Rani (rah-nee), a girl's name meaning queen
Roshan (roh-shuhn), a name meaning light
rupee (roo-pee), a silver coin worth about 20 cents
shabash (shah-bahsh), a word of approval
Shah Jahan (shah juh-hahn), Mogul emperor of India
Shanti (shahn-tee), a girl's name meaning peace
Shera (shay-rah), a boy's name meaning lion
Shirin (shee-reen), a girl's name meaning sweet
Sialkot (see-ahl-koht), a city in Pakistan
Singh (sing), surname of Sikhs and Christians of Sikh origin
sitar (see-tahr), a stringed instrument like a banjo
Sri (sree), Mr.
Srimati (sree-muh-tee), Mrs.
sulwar (sool-vahr), full trousers worn by women and girls in
    the Punjab
Sundar (soon-duhr), a man's name
Sundri (soon-dree), a name meaning beautiful
Sutlej (suht-lidge), a river in Pakistan and the Punjab
Tara (tah-rah), a girl's name meaning star
tawa (tuh-vuh), a thin, curved iron plate for baking bread
tonga (tohn-gah), a two-wheeled cart drawn by a horse
Ustani-ji (oo-stah-nee-jee), a woman teacher
Vijai (vee-jie), a boy's name meaning victory
Yusuf (you-suhf), Joseph

MANUFACTURED IN NEW YORK, N. Y.

COMPOSITION: *The Composing Room, Inc.*
LITHOGRAPHY: *General Offset Company, Inc.*
BINDING: *Cloth, Chas. H. Bohn Company, Inc.*
Paper, Mercury Bookbinding
Service, Inc.
PAPER: *Warren's Old Style Laid*
CLOTH: *Bancroft Arrestox B*
FORMAT: *Louise E. Jefferson*